ELEMENTARY
CRYPTANALYSIS
A
MATHEMATICAL APPROACH

NEW MATHEMATICAL LIBRARY

published by

The Mathematical Association of America

The New Mathematical Library (NML) was begun in 1961 by the School Mathematics Study Group to make available to high school students short expository books on various topics not usually covered in the high school syllabus. In a decade the NML matured into a steadily growing series of some twenty titles of interest not only to the originally intended audience, but to college students and teachers at all levels. Previously published by Random House and L. W. Singer, the NML became a publication series of the Mathematical Association of America (MAA) in 1975. Under the auspices of the MAA the NML will continue to grow and will remain dedicated to its original and expanded purposes.

ELEMENTARY
CRYPTANALYSIS
A
MATHEMATICAL APPROACH

by

Abraham Sinkov

Arizona State University

22

THE MATHEMATICAL ASSOCIATION
OF AMERICA

FOR

Delia, Judy, Michael

Illustrations by George H. Buehler

Second Printing

Library of Congress Catalog Card Number: 72-89953

Manufactured in the United States of America

Note to the Reader

This book is one of a series written by professional mathematicians in order to make some important mathematical ideas interesting and understandable to a large audience of high school students and laymen. Most of the volumes in the *New Mathematical Library* cover topics not usually included in the high school curriculum; they vary in difficulty, and, even within a single book, some parts require a greater degree of concentration than others. Thus, while the reader needs little technical knowledge to understand most of these books, he will have to make an intellectual effort.

If the reader has so far encountered mathematics only in classroom work, he should keep in mind that a book on mathematics cannot be read quickly. Nor must he expect to understand all parts of the book on first reading. He should feel free to skip complicated parts and return to them later; often an argument will be clarified by a subsequent remark. On the other hand, sections containing thoroughly familiar material may be read very quickly.

The best way to learn mathematics is to *do* mathematics, and each book includes problems, some of which may require considerable thought. The reader is urged to acquire the habit of reading with paper and pencil in hand; in this way mathematics will become increasingly meaningful to him.

The authors and editorial committee are interested in reactions to the books in this series and hope that readers will write to: Anneli Lax, Editor, New Mathematical Library, NEW YORK UNIVERSITY, THE COURANT INSTITUTE OF MATHEMATICAL SCIENCES, 251 Mercer Street, New York, N. Y. 10012.

The Editors

NEW MATHEMATICAL LIBRARY

Other titles in preparation

Contents

CONTENTS

Introduction

To a very great extent, mankind owes its progress to the ability to communicate, and a key aspect in this ability is the capability of communicating in writing. From the earliest days of writing, there have been occasions when individuals have desired to limit their information to a restricted group of people. They had secrets they wanted to keep. To this end, such individuals developed ideas by means of which their communications could be made unintelligible to those who had not been provided with the special information needed for decipherment. The general techniques used to accomplish such a purpose, i.e. the hiding of the meaning of messages, constitute the study known as *cryptography*.

Before the development of postal systems and electrical transmission of information, the usual manner of sending a communication was by private messenger. Even under these circumstances the use of the concealment tactics of cryptography was often advisable because of the possibility that the messenger might be apprehended or prove disloyal. In recent times a message transmitted by radio could be copied by anyone having appropriate equipment and listening to the right frequency at the right time. In such a case, if the sender desired privacy of communication he would be required to employ some method of cryptographic concealment.

Now, just as the sender of the message attempted to conceal his information from any but the desired recipient, there would be individuals very much interested in determining what the message said—most probably the very individuals from whom the sender was trying to keep the information. Should such an individual obtain—in one way or another—a copy of the cryptographed message, he would attempt to unravel the secret it carried. But of course his attempt would have to be made without a knowledge of the cryptographic

1

details employed to hide the content. Efforts aimed at reading a secret message in this way come under the heading of the study called *cryptanalysis*.

History abounds with accounts of situations where successful cryptanalysis proved a most important element in achieving diplomatic successes, gaining military victories, apprehending criminals, preventing espionage. Cryptanalysis has contributed to the translation of historical documents which came to light in official archives and were found to be in secret language. It has even aided in the reconstruction of lost languages which had been dead for so long that nothing was known about them so that they were, in effect, secret languages. These aspects of the history and drama of cryptanalysis are adequately treated in many other sources, and are not discussed in this book.

The purpose of this monograph is to introduce the reader to some of the basic techniques of cryptanalysis. The method used is to describe a cryptographic procedure and then to examine how its details can possibly be reconstructed without any information about them. The appreciation of what can be accomplished analytically may then suggest methods of improving the cryptography by eliminating the deficiencies exploited in the cryptanalysis. Such improvement then poses a new problem for the analyst. This step by step improvement has in fact been the history of the development of *cryptology*—the word used generically to embrace both cryptography and cryptanalysis.

The analytical processes used by a cryptanalyst require a number of techniques: some mathematical, some linguistic, some of an engineering character, and even some not readily describable such as luck, flair, sixth sense, etc. Since this book is being written essentially for students of mathematics, the presentation will emphasize mathematical aspects of cryptanalysis. Some of the other aspects will naturally enter into the general discussion, but for the most part the emphasis will be on mathematical features. And since the mathematical concepts introduced relate to branches of mathematics not usually studied in high school, they will be treated in some detail as they are introduced.

It is to be appreciated that the emphasis on mathematical procedures has resulted in the omission of some other topics. For example, nothing is said about codes which are dictionary type books used to convert plain language into secret language.

The descriptions of methods of solution will be provided by applications to specific examples. These have been selected in such a way as to simplify the exposition. The texts have been taken almost entirely from newspaper articles. They have been chosen of sufficient length so that the difficulty of solution would not be excessive. No attempt has been made to modify the language or the frequencies of any of the letters.

As the title implies, the cryptographic systems studied in this book are elementary. They have been well known and used for a long time. The methods of solution have also been well known, although their presentation has not usually been in mathematical terms. The reader will become aware that the cryptography studied here can be made more sophisticated. Ideas on improving the systems described are certain to come to his mind. The most significant types of recent advances have come with the introduction of machines—electromechanical and electronic—and have given cryptographic systems a much more complicated character. Methods for solution of such systems must be correspondingly more advanced. All that we can hope to accomplish in this book is to provide some of the fundamental techniques which are the basis of cryptanalytic endeavor.

It is important that the reader understand each step in the reasoning presented and that he confirm what is done in the text by studying it in detail if he wishes to achieve the kind of skill needed to deal independently with cryptanalytic problems.

I should acknowledge here my thanks to Mrs. Anneli Lax, Editor of the SMSG monograph series, for her many useful suggestions during the writing of this monograph, and to Dr. Solomon Kullback, for assistance in some aspects of the mathematical statistics involved. My chief indebtedness is to my wife, a good cryptanalyst in her own right, for her encouragement and for her handling of much of the detail that had to be coped with.

CHAPTER ONE

Monoalphabetic Ciphers Using Direct Standard Alphabets

1.1 The Caesar Cipher

One of the earliest cryptographic systems known was used by Julius Caesar and is referred to by his name—the Caesar Cipher. It consisted of a replacement of each letter of the message by the letter three places beyond it in the normal alphabet. Caesar used the Roman alphabet, of course, but we shall illustrate his procedure with our own present day alphabet.

Suppose it is desired to encipher† the message:

I CAME I SAW I CONQUERED

Under each letter of the message we write the letter three places further along in the alphabet; thus, I is replaced by L, C by F, A by D, etc. The complete process yields

```
I CAME I SAW I CONQUERED
L FDPH L VDZ L FRQTXHUHG
```

---

† The process of converting a message from plain language into secret language by systematic treatment of its letters is called *enciphering*; the inverse process of restoring the original message from the cipher text by reversing the steps of encipherment with full knowledge of the details is called *deciphering*.

and the cipher message is:

L FDPH L VDZ L FRQTXHUHG

The result looks quite unintelligible. To one examining it who had no notion of how it has been produced, it could prove quite baffling. On the other hand, to one who knows the secret, it is quickly unraveled. Just replace each letter of the cipher by the letter three places preceding it in the normal alphabet, and the plain language is revealed.

This is an example of a type of cipher called a *substitution cipher* in which each letter of the original message is replaced by another. A convenient way to represent this substitution is by means of a *substitution alphabet* which indicates the letter by letter replacement. The way to produce the substitution alphabet of the Caesar Cipher is to write out the normal alphabetic sequence on one line, and then to rewrite it on a second line, but starting with D instead of A. When the end of the alphabet is reached in the lower line, the letter Z is followed by A, B, C, as though the alphabet represented a continuous repetitive cycle:

Plain   A B C D E F G H I J K L M N O P Q R S T U V W X Y Z

Cipher   D E F G H I J K L M N O P Q R S T U V W X Y Z A B C

We call the upper line of the substitution alphabet the *plain sequence* and the lower line the *cipher sequence*.

With this arrangement, the enciphering procedure can be performed by replacing each letter of the plain language message by the letter below it in the substitution alphabet; decipherment consists of replacing each letter of the cipher message by the letter above it in the substitution alphabet. (Mathematically, we say that the deciphering procedure is the inverse operation to that of encipherment.)

The cryptographic process represented by the Caesar Cipher can be carried out numerically. Suppose we associate each letter with the number representing its position in the normal sequence. We would have the correspondence:

A B C D E F G H I J K L M N O P Q R S T U V W X Y Z
1 2 3 4 5 6 7 8 9 10 11 12 13 14 15 16 17 18 19 20 21 22 23 24 25 26

Now, to encipher the message **I CAME I SAW I CONQUERED**, we proceed as follows (each step is illustrated below):

(i) Replace each letter by the number to which it corresponds.

(ii) Add 3 to each of these numbers.

(iii) Replace the resulting numbers by their letter equivalents in the letter-number correspondences.

```
          I   C A M  E   I   S  A W   I   C  O  N  Q  U  E  R  E D
  (i):    9   3 1 13 5   9   19 1 23  9   3  15 14 17 21 5  18 5 4
 (ii):    12  6 4 16 8   12  22 4 26  12  6  18 17 20 24 8  21 8 7
(iii):    L   F D P  H   L   V  D Z   L   F  R  Q  T  X  H  U  H G
```

The result, as it should be, is the same cipher message as was previously derived.

Exercises

Decipher the following messages which were enciphered by means of the Caesar Cipher:

1. FRZDUGV GLH PDQB WLPHV EHIRUH WKHLU GHDWKV

2. WKH HYLO WKDW PHQ GR OLYHV DIWHU WKHP

1.2 Modular arithmetic

One problem may arise in connection with performing the encipherment numerically. Suppose we need to encipher X, Y, or Z whose numerical equivalents are 24, 25, 26, respectively. The addition of 3 to these numbers yields 27, 28, 29, no one of which is included in our letter-number correspondence. If we look back to our substitution alphabet we see that X, Y, Z are enciphered by A, B, C, so that the numbers 27, 28, 29 are considered to correspond to the same letters as the numbers 1, 2, 3. Because we treated the cipher sequence as a continuous cycle, we are in effect replacing numbers greater than 26 by the results obtained when 26 is subtracted from them. There can be no ambiguity, since the letters A, B, C occur in the cipher sequence only under the letters X, Y, Z, respectively, so the one-to-one nature of the correspondence is preserved also in the numerical representations.

We shall make this idea of equivalent numbers a general type of procedure in the arithmetic of cryptography. We might agree, for example, to work only with the integers 1 to 26, and with the understanding that any positive integer a outside the set $\{1, 2, 3, \cdots, 26\}$ is reducible to an equivalent integer b within the set. It is clear that this is always possible. Divide a by 26, and the remainder (or residue) will be the number b. If the remainder is zero, that is, if a is a multiple of 26, then we set b equal to 26.

Examples: If a is 73, we divide by 26 and get a quotient of 2, a remainder of 21. In this case, then, $b = 21$. If a is 130, we divide by 26, get a quotient of 5 and a remainder of 0; in this case $b = 26$.

In general, if an integer a is greater than 26, we can write it, as a result of dividing by 26, in the form

$$a = k(26) + b,$$

where b is in the set $\{1, 2, \cdots, 26\}$. In our examples we have $73 = 2(26) + 21$ and $130 = 5(26) = 4(26) + 26$.

We treat a and b as being equivalent and we say that a is *congruent* to b. Another way of saying it is: *two numbers a and b are congruent if their difference $a - b$ is a multiple of 26.* By this definition, 0 is congruent to 26; in fact, we could, and sometimes do, consider our arithmetic as consisting of the numbers 0 to 25 instead of 1 to 26. In the most general sense, any set of 26 numbers congruent to the numbers 1 to 26 could be used as the desired set. Such a set of numbers is called a *complete set of residues.* There are instances when a complete set of residues other than the first 26 numbers is useful. For cryptographic purposes we will work almost exclusively with the complete set of residues 1 to 26.

Even if a were negative, we could easily find a positive number b in the set $\{1, 2, \cdots, 26\}$ such that a is congruent to b: Divide the positive number $-a$ by 26, obtaining

$$-a = q(26) + r = (q + 1)26 - (26 - r), \qquad q \geq 0, \quad 0 \leq r < 26.$$

We now set

$$b = 26 - r,$$

so that

$$a = -(q + 1)26 + b.$$

Clearly, b is congruent to a by our definition since

$$a - b = -(q + 1)26$$

is a multiple of 26; moreover, b is in the set $\{1, 2, \cdots, 26\}$ since $b = 26 - r$ and $0 \leq r < 26$. So, for negative a, we simply let b be the number $26 - r$, where r is the remainder obtained when $-a$ is divided by 26.

Examples: 1. $a = -58$, $-a = 2(26) + 6$, $b = 26 - 6 = 20$; -58 is congruent to 20.

      2. $a = -3$, $-a = 0(26) + 3$, $b = 26 - 3 = 23$; -3 is congruent to 23.

In summary, any whole number a—positive, zero, or negative—can be written in the form

$$a = \pm k(26) + b,$$

with b in the set $\{1, 2, \cdots, 26\}$, and a congruent to b.

We see then that it is possible in this arithmetic of cryptography to perform any operations of addition, subtraction, or multiplication on integers, and to reduce the answer always to one of the numbers in the complete set of residues. (Division is more involved; it will be discussed later on.)

It should be mentioned here that this type of arithmetic has wide applicability in many branches of mathematics where the numbers considered are integers. It is called *modular arithmetic*, and any positive integer may be chosen as the modulus, i.e. the role played by 26 in the discussion above. If the modulus is the number n, for example, then we can think of our arithmetic as involving only n numbers. These may be any n consecutive integers, for example 0 to $n - 1$, or 1 to n. Having chosen such a set, we can reduce every integer, positive or negative, to a number in the selected set. If a is reducible by this process to b, we say that a *is congruent to b modulo n,* and we write that statement in symbols as

$$a \equiv b \pmod{n},$$

and mean that

$$a - b = k \cdot n, \quad \text{where } k \text{ is an integer.}$$

It is a kind of equality. As far as addition and subtraction are concerned, the congruence symbol ($\equiv$) acts like an equal sign.

If

$$a \equiv b \pmod{n} \quad \text{and} \quad c \equiv d \pmod{n},$$

then

$$a + c \equiv b + d \pmod{n} \quad \text{and} \quad a - c \equiv b - d \pmod{n}.$$

To prove this, we just translate this symbolism as follows: If

$$a - b = kn,$$
$$c - d = ln,$$

then

$$(a + c) - (b + d) = (k + l)n$$

and

$$(a - c) - (b - d) = (k - l)n.$$

If we have a congruence of the form

$$x + a \equiv b \pmod{n},$$

its solution is

$$x \equiv b - a \pmod{n},$$

because the first relation says $x + a - b = x - (b - a)$ is a multiple of n, so x is congruent to $b - a$. Every congruence of the form $x \pm k \equiv a \pmod{n}$ with fixed integers a, k and n has a unique solution, viz. $x \equiv a \mp k$.

Because our alphabet contains 26 letters, the number 26 will most frequently be the modulus we shall use in cryptography.

Exercises

3. (a) If the first day of a month is Monday, what day of the week is represented by dates congruent to 3 modulo 7 during that month?
(b) What fraction of a pound is involved in any weight which is a number of ounces congruent to 20 modulo 16?

4. Solve $x + 12 \equiv 3 \pmod 5$.

5. Solve $y - 1 \equiv 13 \pmod 6$.

1.3   Direct standard alphabets

We don't know why Caesar selected the number 3 as the amount of shift between the cipher sequence and the plain sequence. He could have chosen any number at all, so long as an understanding had been made with his correspondent about how the enciphering was to be accomplished. In fact, given a proper agreement, the amount of shift could change from message to message. For example, it could be prearranged that a number be assigned to each message by some agreed scheme—as illustrations, we could mention the number of words in the message, or a serial number associated with the message, or the date of the month when the message was sent, or a number selected by a process having no connection at all with the actual communication—and then this number, reduced modulo 26, would be the number of places of shift. Given this number, the substitution alphabet can be constructed and used for encipherment or for decipherment. A substitution alphabet in which both the plain and the cipher sequences are the normal alphabet (with the cipher sequence shifted a specific number of places) is called a *direct standard alphabet*. In the equivalent numerical process, expressible as $C = P + K$, the number of places of shift (K) is the number to be added to the numerical equivalent of each plain language character (P) to determine its cipher replacement (C). If the number of positions of shift is K, then the letter A in the plain sequence will be opposite the letter corresponding to $1 + K$ in the cipher sequence.

The construction of direct standard alphabets can be readily accomplished by a simple device, made of two concentric circles, each of which has the alphabet inscribed around its circumference (Figure 1). The outer ring is the plain sequence and the inner ring, which can be rotated, is the cipher sequence. If we set against A of the outer ring, the letter corresponding to $1 + K$ on the inner ring, we have the substitution alphabet for which the shift is K. (In Figure 1, $K = 6$.)

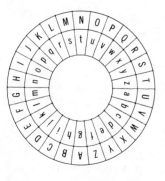

Figure 1

It is interesting to note that a similar device was used many years ago by the U. S. Army. The alphabets it produced differed from direct standard alphabets in that the cipher sequence was written backwards. Such a sequence is called a *reversed standard sequence*, and the alphabet it produces when set against a normal plain sequence is a *reversed standard alphabet*.

The disk for constructing direct standard alphabets makes it possible, by the proper setting of the inner circle, to select any one of the 26 direct standard alphabets. This same capability was achieved in a different way by the French cryptographer Vigenère. He wrote out a square in which the top row was the normal sequence and each succeeding row was obtained by shifting the sequence one letter to the left. By putting the normal alphabet across the top of the square as the plain sequence, any direct standard alphabet was obtainable by combining the plain sequence with the appropriate row within the square. Each of these alphabets could be simply designated by its first letter.

The Vigenère square is shown on the next page (Fig. 2). It is the basis of the systems which we shall study in Chapter 3.

One minor precaution is necessary in connection with the idea of prearranging the amount of shift to be used. It would be an obvious mistake to permit the number which determines the key for any message to be a multiple of 26, since such a number reduced modulo 26 becomes zero, and as a result the cipher would be identical with the plain language. The prearrangement must not permit the number 26 (or any multiple of it) to be used as the amount of shift; should such a number arise as a result of the selection process which is being used, it would have to be replaced by some other agreed number.

```
Plain    A B C D E F G H I J K L M N O P Q R S T U V W X Y Z

         A B C D E F G H I J K L M N O P Q R S T U V W X Y Z
         B C D E F G H I J K L M N O P Q R S T U V W X Y Z A
         C D E F G H I J K L M N O P Q R S T U V W X Y Z A B
         D E F G H I J K L M N O P Q R S T U V W X Y Z A B C
         E F G H I J K L M N O P Q R S T U V W X Y Z A B C D
         F G H I J K L M N O P Q R S T U V W X Y Z A B C D E
         G H I J K L M N O P Q R S T U V W X Y Z A B C D E F
         H I J K L M N O P Q R S T U V W X Y Z A B C D E F G
         I J K L M N O P Q R S T U V W X Y Z A B C D E F G H
         J K L M N O P Q R S T U V W X Y Z A B C D E F G H I
      c  K L M N O P Q R S T U V W X Y Z A B C D E F G H I J
      i  L M N O P Q R S T U V W X Y Z A B C D E F G H I J K
      p  M N O P Q R S T U V W X Y Z A B C D E F G H I J K L
      h  N O P Q R S T U V W X Y Z A B C D E F G H I J K L M
      e  O P Q R S T U V W X Y Z A B C D E F G H I J K L M N
      r  P Q R S T U V W X Y Z A B C D E F G H I J K L M N O
         Q R S T U V W X Y Z A B C D E F G H I J K L M N O P
         R S T U V W X Y Z A B C D E F G H I J K L M N O P Q
         S T U V W X Y Z A B C D E F G H I J K L M N O P Q R
         T U V W X Y Z A B C D E F G H I J K L M N O P Q R S
         U V W X Y Z A B C D E F G H I J K L M N O P Q R S T
         V W X Y Z A B C D E F G H I J K L M N O P Q R S T U
         W X Y Z A B C D E F G H I J K L M N O P Q R S T U V
         X Y Z A B C D E F G H I J K L M N O P Q R S T U V W
         Y Z A B C D E F G H I J K L M N O P Q R S T U V W X
         Z A B C D E F G H I J K L M N O P Q R S T U V W X Y
```

Figure 2

The essential elements of any cryptographic system are two: the general procedure to be used and its detailed implementation. The general procedure is called the *general system* and the details are called the *specific key*. Thus, the Caesar Cipher is a direct standard alphabet with the specific key 3. Since only one substitution alphabet is employed by the system, the result is called a *monoalphabetic cipher*.

Exercises

6. (a) Construct the direct standard alphabet for which the shift is 7, and encipher the message:

THE FAULT DEAR BRUTUS IS NOT IN OUR STARS BUT IN OURSELVES

(b) Decipher the following monoalphabetic cipher knowing that it is a direct standard alphabet with shift 11:

ESPCP TD L ETOP TY ESP LQQLTCD ZQ XPY HSTNS ELVPY LE ESP QWZZO WPLOD ZY EZ QZCEFYP

1.4 Solution of direct standard alphabets by completing the plain component

Now that we understand how a message can be enciphered by the use of a direct standard alphabet, we consider the solution of a message which has been enciphered in that way. We take the following message as an example:

BPM VMOWBQIBQWVA NWZ I AMBBTMUMVB WN BPM ABZQSM
IZM IB IV QUXIAAM ZMKWUUMVL EM QVKZMIAM WCZ WNNMZ

We are going to put ourselves in the position of a cryptanalyst who has obtained a copy of this cipher message and wishes to solve it. We shall furthermore suppose that in some way—perhaps a lucky guess, perhaps because he knows something of the correspondence habits of the sender—the cryptanalyst knows the general system, but lacks the specific key. In this situation, then, all he has to do is to determine one number in order to be able to read the message, the number representing the amount of shift of the cipher sequence against the plain sequence.

From this point of view, the problem doesn't sound very difficult. After all, there are only 25 possible numbers, and each one can be tried in turn until the correct one discloses the plain language. Indeed, just working with one word might be enough to determine the specific key.

Thus, suppose we take the first word of the message: BPM. The numerical equivalents of these letters are 2 16 13. If we subtract 1 from each of these numbers, we have

$$1\ 15\ 12\ =\ A\ O\ L$$

If we subtract 2 from each of the original numbers, we have

$$26\ 14\ 11\ =\ Z\ N\ K$$

We continue this process, and organize the results in the form of a table. Starting with 2 16 13, we obtain the information tabulated below.

Subtract	Get			Corresponding to letters		
1	1	15	12	A	O	L
2	26	14	11	Z	N	K
3	25	13	10	Y	M	J
4	24	12	9	X	L	I
5	23	11	8	W	K	H
6	22	10	7	V	J	G
7	21	9	6	U	I	F
8	20	8	5	T	H	E

When we reach the number 8, we see the word THE, which looks good. And, in fact, if we now apply the key 8 to the message as a whole, we are able to read the entire communication. (The reader should go through the details of decipherment in order to get used to the cryptographic process.)

Note that if we had not stopped our subtraction process when the word THE appeared, but had continued through the entire set of numbers 1 to 25, each column on the right would have been a complete alphabet reading in reversed order. We can make that alphabet read in direct order, if we like, by testing the possible key numbers in reverse, i.e. we try 25 first, then 24, etc. This now suggests a slightly different method of hunting for the key number.

We illustrate this by taking another word of the cipher message, say the word

A B Z Q S M

Starting with each letter in turn, we write the complete alphabet under it:

```
A  B  Z  Q  S  M
B  C  A  R  T  N
C  D  B  S  U  O
D  E  C  T  V  P
E  F  D  U  W  Q
F  G  E  V  X  R
G  H  F  W  Y  S
H  I  G  X  Z  T
I  J  H  Y  A  U
J  K  I  Z  B  V
K  L  J  A  C  W
L  M  K  B  D  X
M  N  L  C  E  Y
N  O  M  D  F  Z
O  P  N  E  G  A
P  Q  O  F  H  B
Q  R  P  G  I  C
R  S  Q  H  J  D
S  T  R  I  K  E
T  U  S  J  L  F
U  V  T  K  M  G
V  W  U  L  N  H
W  X  V  M  O  I
X  Y  W  N  P  J
Y  Z  X  O  Q  K
Z  A  Y  P  R  L
```

Then we look for a line that might represent good text, and we find the word STRIKE. We then check what key number it corresponds to. Since the cipher letter A is 1 and the plain letter S corresponding to it is 19, the key number K must be such that $19 + K \equiv 1 \pmod{26}$. That means that $K \equiv 1 - 19 \equiv -18 \equiv 8 \pmod{26}$.

This process of finding the key to a cipher message by writing the entire alphabet for each of a series of cipher letters is called *completing the plain component*.

It has been assumed in the solution of the preceding message that the general system of encipherment was that of a direct standard alphabet. In other words, the general system of cryptography that had been used in the encipherment was taken for granted. The analysis then consisted in determining the single unknown quantity, the specific key, which gives the number of positions of shift of the cipher sequence against the plain sequence. That the assumption was appropriate is demonstrated by the fact that it permitted the original message to be reconstructed. And this is clearly the ultimate criterion of success in cryptanalysis: "Can you read the message?"

Exercises

Solve the following messages:

7. VXMDUJA JARCQVNCRL LXDUM KN LXWBRMNANM ANVJRWMNA
JARCQVNCRL

8. MZVYDIB DN OJ OCZ HDIY RCVO ZSZMXDNZ DN OJ OCZ WJYT

1.5   Solving direct standard alphabets by frequency considerations

We now examine the possibility of a different method of procedure which does not assume, but instead will prove, that the system of encipherment used a shift of the normal alphabet. This method is based on a fundamental property of language, the relative frequencies of occurrence of the different letters of the alphabet.

Suppose we take a sample of plain text, say a page of a book or some paragraphs from a newspaper, and we make a count of the frequency of each letter, that is, the number of times each letter appears. By way of illustration, a sample, 1000 letters long, produced the following count:

A	73	J	2	S	63
B	9	K	3	T	93
C	30	L	35	U	27
D	44	M	25	V	13
E	130	N	78	W	16
F	28	O	74	X	5
G	16	P	27	Y	19
H	35	Q	3	Z	1
I	74	R	77		

We are interested in the percentage of occurrence of each letter, i.e. its *relative frequency*. Since the total number of letters in this sample is 1000, the relative frequency of each letter is obtained by dividing its actual frequency by 10. As would be expected, the relative frequencies differ for different letters. The number of E's is 13% of the total. The number of T's is approximately 9%. The vowels A, I, O each occur about 7%; some letters like G, V, W, Y appear very infrequently (between 1 and 2 percent) while J, K, Q, and Z appear almost not at all.

To say that the relative frequency of E is 13% means that the chance of getting an E by a random selection from the total 1000 letters is 13 out of 100. We therefore use the word *probability* whose precise mathematical definition is based on the idea of relative frequency, and we use the notation

$$P_E = .13$$

to mean that the probability of getting an E is 13%. In this notation, $P_T = .09$, $P_A = .07$, etc. Since the sum of all the frequencies is the number of letters in the sample, it follows that the sum of the relative frequencies is 100 percent, that is 1, and hence that the sum of the probabilities for all the 26 letters is 1:

$$P_A + P_B + P_C + \cdots + P_Z = 1.$$

A shorthand notation for this statement is

$$\sum_{i=A}^{i=Z} P_i = 1.$$

The expression on the left is read "the sum of the quantities P_i as i takes on, in turn, all the values from A to Z". A is called the lower limit and Z the upper limit of the summation.

The same general picture as we found from our sample of 1000 letters would result from the examination of any reasonably long plain language text. The relative frequencies of the individual letters would vary from selection to selection depending on a number of considerations such as the subject matter, the choice of language and the style of writing. But the basic fact remains that some letters, in particular the vowels and a few consonants like T, N, R, S, have relatively high frequencies, while others, such as J, K, Q, V, W, X, Y, Z, occur with relatively low frequencies. And the percentage of occurrence of any particular letter, which we shall call its *characteristic frequency*, does not usually vary widely from selection to selection. If a message is very short, the actual frequency of some letters in that message might vary substantially from the characteristic frequencies. The longer the message, the less likely is it that there will be wide variation from the characteristic frequencies.

Suppose we represent the information in the frequency count of page 16 in the form of a bar graph. For purposes of simplification we shall round off each of the percentages to the nearest whole number so that the characteristic frequency of each letter can be shown by tally marks as in the presentation below.

```
A  B  C  D  E  F  G  H  I  J  K  L  M  N  O  P  Q  R  S  T  U  V  W  X  Y  Z
≠  -  =  =  ≠  =  -  =  ≠           =  =  ≠  ≠  =     ≠  ≠  ≠  =  -  =     =
=        ≠           =                 =  =           =  -  =
≡
```

We see in this kind of presentation a clearer picture of the highs and lows in the characteristic frequencies of the letters than is evident from examining the table of figures. And there is a pattern about it which is important. Among the high frequencies we see the evenly spaced A, E, and I (four letters apart) with E the most frequent of all the letters, the consecutive pair N, O, and the consecutive triplet R, S, T. In the low frequencies we have the consecutive pair J, K and the string U, V, W, X, Y, Z.

This pattern of highs and lows, with the indicated spacings, characterizes the normal alphabet in plain language. It is a basic tool of cryptanalysis.

Consider now what happens when a message is enciphered by shifting the normal alphabet against itself. For the sake of illustration, suppose that the shift is eight letters. Then any time the letter A appears in the plain language, it will be replaced by I. A convenient notation, which we shall use, is to designate plain language letters with the subscript p and cipher letters with the subscript c. Thus the fact that plain A is replaced by cipher I would be written $A_p = I_c$. Any time B appears it will be replaced by J; $B_p = J_c$. Each letter of the original message will always be replaced by the same equivalent every time it appears. The result is that the frequency distribution of the cipher message will be the same as that of the original plain language message except for the fact that there has been a shift of 8 positions. If the specific key had been some other number n, the distribution would have been shifted n positions.

We return now to the cipher message on page 13 and make a frequency count of the letters in the message. A simple way to do this is to write out the alphabet and then go through the cipher message letter by letter, making a tally mark for each letter as it is encountered. Cross-section (graph) paper is helpful, and the tallies can be grouped in fives by making each fifth one at right angles as shown on page 18. When this process is completed for the cipher message, we have the following distribution:

A B C D E F G H I J K L M N O P Q R S T U V W X Y Z

Since this graph tells us the frequencies of individual letters, it is called a *monographic frequency distribution*. We look in this distribution for the normal alphabet pattern, and we note:

I, M, Q (all of high frequency) are four spaces apart, with M the most frequent of all the letters;

V, W is a high pair;

Z, A, B is a high triplet;

C, D, E, F, G, H form a long string of consecutive letters with low frequencies.

All of these facts fit the picture of a direct standard alphabet provided we make $I_c = A_p$; the letter I in this distribution must correspond to A of the normal alphabet.

Another way of seeing this fact is to slide the cipher distribution against the plain language distribution until the two match each other. We first write out the plain language distribution, and to allow for overlap, we write it twice. Then we put the cipher distribution against it and slide the cipher one position at a time until we get a good match of highs against highs and lows against lows. If we put the plain and the cipher distributions on separate sheets, it simplifies sliding the cipher distribution against the plain distribution. We start with A_c against B_p (see Figure 3). In this position we see a few places where high frequencies match high frequencies as, for example, N_p, M_c; O_p, N_c; R_p, Q_c; A_p, Z_c. And there are a few places where low frequencies match one another: K_p, J_c; Y_p, X_c; Z_p, Y_c. But there are serious disagreements: E_p, the most frequent letter is opposite one which doesn't occur at all; and B_p, A_c; I_p, H_c; S_p, R_c; T_p, S_c; X_p, W_c are all very poor matches. We are led to conclude that this is not a correct positioning of the two distributions.

We then shift the cipher distribution so that $A_c = C_p$ and compare the two distributions (Figure 4). Again we conclude that we do not have a good match.

We continue the process, getting unsatisfactory matching, until we reach $A_c = S_p$ (Figure 5). In this position, we see that we have found a good match. High frequency letters in one distribution are opposite high frequency letters in the other; low frequency letters are opposite low frequency letters. There isn't a single contradictory pair. Given this agreement of the two frequency patterns, we conclude that the general system was that of a direct standard alphabet, and that in the correct substitution alphabet $A_p = I_c$. The substitution alphabet itself results from the matching positions of the two frequenc distributions. When it is applied to the cipher message it will produce plain language, the final proof of correctness.

Exercises

Solve the following messages by matching against the normal frequency distribution:

9. CQSOB KOHSF WG PZIS PSQOIGS RWFH DOFHWQZSG WB HVS KOHSF
   FSTZSQH GIBZWUVH PIH HVS KOHSF OPGCFPG FSR OBR MSZZCK
   HVS UFSSBG OBR PZISG HVOH OFS ZSTH AOYS HVS RSSD PZIS
   CQSOB

10. SNHPJQ NX F MJFAD XNQAJW BMNYJ RJYFQQNH JQJRJSY NY NX
    RFLSJYNH YFPJX F MNLM UTQNXM FSI ITJX STY YFWSNXM TW
    WZXY JFXNQD

Plain

Cipher

Figure 3 $A_c = B_p$

Plain

Cipher

Figure 4 $A_c = C_p$

Plain

Cipher

Figure 5 $A_c = S_p$

1.6 Alphabets based on decimations of the normal sequence

It is evident from the relative ease with which the Caesar Cipher—or its generalization to an arbitrary number of positions of shift—has been solved, that such a system offers very little security.

Let us think up a different method of enciphering a message. Instead of adding a key number to the equivalents of the plain language letters, we shall multiply by the key number. As a simple illustration, we use the key number 2.

We proceed in a manner similar to the procedure on page 6:

(i) Replace each letter of the alphabet by the number to which it corresponds.

(ii) Multiply each number by 2; if the answer exceeds 26, replace it by the equivalent residue.

(iii) Substitute for the resulting numbers their letter equivalents to derive the cipher sequence.

```
Plain:    A  B  C  D  E  F  G  H  I  J  K  L  M
   (i):   1  2  3  4  5  6  7  8  9 10 11 12 13
  (ii):   2  4  6  8 10 12 14 16 18 20 22 24 26
Residue:  2  4  6  8 10 12 14 16 18 20 22 24 26
 (iii):   B  D  F  H  J  L  N  P  R  T  V  X  Z

Plain:    N  O  P  Q  R  S  T  U  V  W  X  Y  Z
   (i):  14 15 16 17 18 19 20 21 22 23 24 25 26
  (ii):  28 30 32 34 36 38 40 42 44 46 48 50 52
Residue:  2  4  6  8 10 12 14 16 18 20 22 24 26
 (iii):   B  D  F  H  J  L  N  P  R  T  V  X  Z
```

The substitution alphabet which results is:

```
Plain:  A B C D E F G H I J K L M N O P Q R S T U V W X Y Z

Cipher: B D F H J L N P R T V X Z B D F H J L N P R T V X Z
```

This is not an acceptable substitution alphabet. Each cipher letter which appears has two occurrences and is the equivalent therefore of two different plain language letters. Decipherment would not be a unique process: there would be two plain language possibilities for each cipher letter. This is unacceptable in a communication system, since there would be situations with different possible decipherments and no way of deciding which of them the sender wanted to convey.

How did this lack of uniqueness come about? The answer is that multiplication by 2 always produces an even number, and since the modulus is even, the residue of an even number must always be even. If a is even, say $a = 2c$, then the relation

$$a = b + k(26)$$

shows that

$$b = 2c - k(26) = 2[c - k(13)]$$

is even. So as x (the numerical equivalent of the plain letter) takes on the values 1 to 26, $2x$ (the cipher value) produces only the even numbers 2, 4, 6, $\cdots$, 26, each one twice. It is not possible to obtain a complete set of residues from this process.

If we used any other even number not divisible by 26 as a multiplier, the same kind of situation would result. Only 13 different cipher letters would enter into the substitution alphabet.

If we tried to multiply by 13, the situation would be even worse. There would be only two possible residues for the entire alphabet, viz. 13 and 26. For, multiplying any odd number by 13 would yield a result congruent to 13, because any odd number can be written in the form $2n + 1$, where n is an integer, and multiplying it by 13 gives $26n + 13$, which is congruent to 13. Any even number, $2n$, multiplied by 13, gives $26n$, which is congruent to 26.

What causes the difficulty is the fact that 2 and 13 are divisors of 26. Any number which has 2 or 13 as a factor would fail to produce a complete set of residues (mod 26) if it were used as a multiplier.

We see here that multiplication in modular arithmetic has some peculiarities which make it different from ordinary multiplication. In particular, since any odd multiple of 13 is congruent to any other odd multiple of 13, it follows that ax can be congruent to bx without a being congruent to b. This is not true of ordinary equality. This means, in the inverse procedure, that a problem in division may have more than one answer in modular arithmetic. For example, if $2x \equiv 2 \pmod{26}$, then $x = 1$ and $x = 14$ are both solutions.

For any general modulus n, a multiplier a when applied in turn to the numbers 1 to n will fail to produce a complete set of residues if a and n have any factors in common. If, however, a and n are relatively prime (i.e. have no common factors) this problem does not arise. In such a case, if we let x be equal to $1, 2, \cdots, n-1, n$ in turn, the product ax will produce all of these same numbers $(1, 2, \cdots, n)$ although in a different order. There will not be any duplications.

Before we prove this statement, let us illustrate it by a simple example. Let 12 be the modulus and 5 the multiplier. Multiply the numbers $1, 2, \cdots, 12$ by 5, and reduce the products modulo 12:

	1	2	3	4	5	6	7	8	9	10	11	12
Multiply by 5:	5	10	15	20	25	30	35	40	45	50	55	60
Residues:	5	10	3	8	1	6	11	4	9	2	7	12

The line of residues contains all the numbers from 1 to 12 in a rearranged order.

We now prove: *if the multiplier a and the modulus n are relatively prime, then all the residues derived from $a, 2a, 3a, \cdots, na$ are distinct.*

Suppose a has no factor in common with n. Suppose also that x and y are different numbers of the set $\{1, 2, \cdots, n\}$, with x less than y. In symbols this is written $1 \le x < y \le n$. We wish to prove that ax is not congruent to $ay \pmod{n}$.

Suppose

$$ay \equiv ax \pmod{n} \qquad a, n \text{ relatively prime.}$$

Then

$$ay - ax \equiv 0 \pmod{n}.$$

From the definition of modular congruence, this means that $ay - ax$ is a multiple of n, say kn:

$$ay - ax = a(y - x) = kn.$$

Since a has no factor in common with n, $y - x$ must have all the factors of n; that is, $y - x$ is a multiple of n.[†] But since

---

† This is a consequence of the Fundamental Theorem of Arithmetic, which assures us that there is only one way of factoring n, a, $y-x$ into primes. For a proof of this consequence, see e.g. Theorem 4.2 in I. Niven's *Numbers: Rational and Irrational*, NML vol. 1, Random House (1961) pp. 57–58.

$1 \leq x < y \leq n$, we have $0 < y - x < n$, so $y - x$ cannot be a multiple of n. This contradiction shows that, if a is prime to the modulus, and if x and y are different numbers of the basic set of residues, then ax is not congruent to ay.

It follows that every congruence of the form $ax \equiv b$ (mod n), with given relatively prime integers a and n, has a unique solution. For, as x takes on the values $1, 2, \cdots, n$ in turn, ax has n distinct residues (no two can be equal by what we just proved); each of these is in the set $\{1, 2, \cdots, n\}$. Therefore, the residue b (also in this set) is covered by exactly one of the distinct residues of ax, and the x which yields it is our unique solution of $ax \equiv b$ (mod n).

If n is not very big, the number x can be obtained by trying the different possibilities 1 to n, one at a time.

Examples: 1. $3x \equiv 1$ (mod 7)   2. $4x \equiv 2$ (mod 5)
$$x = 5 \qquad\qquad\qquad x = 3$$

There are general methods of solving such congruences, but they are beyond the scope of this book. This does not mean that the reader is limited to testing consecutive numbers, one at a time, until he finds the right one. It is possible to convert the given congruence into an equivalent one by multiplying it by a number prime to the modulus. Choose the multiplier so as to reduce the magnitude of the coefficient of x. Repeat this process with the new congruence and continue reducing the coefficient of x until it becomes 1 or -1.

To illustrate, suppose we wish to solve

$$19x \equiv 1 \pmod{26}.$$

Since $19 \equiv -7$ (mod 26), we may write

$$-7x \equiv 1 \pmod{26}.$$

Multiply by 3, obtaining

$$-21x \equiv 3 \pmod{26},$$

and since

$$-21 \equiv 5 \pmod{26},$$

write

$$5x \equiv 3 \pmod{26}.$$

Multiply by 5, obtaining

$$25x \equiv 15 \ (\mathrm{mod}\ 26),$$

and use

$$25 \equiv -1 \ (\mathrm{mod}\ 26)$$

to get

$$-x \equiv 15 \ (\mathrm{mod}\ 26).$$

Multiply by -1 to find the solution

$$x \equiv -15 \equiv 11 \ (\mathrm{mod}\ 26).$$

The solution x of the congruence $ax \equiv 1 \ (\mathrm{mod}\ n)$ is called the *inverse* of a with respect to multiplication, and may be denoted by a^{-1}. It is also called the reciprocal, by analogy with the same idea in ordinary arithmetic. Thus the above example shows that the reciprocal of 19 (mod 26) is 11. A number has a reciprocal in modular arithmetic if and only if it is prime to the modulus.

If we have a table of reciprocals modulo 26, then a simple solution of $ax \equiv b \ (\mathrm{mod}\ 26)$ is immediately obtainable just by forming the product of b and the reciprocal a^{-1} of a, since

$$x \equiv a^{-1}b \ (\mathrm{mod}\ 26).$$

Let us return now to the idea of constructing a substitution alphabet by multiplication, and consider the number 3 as a multiplier.

Plain:	A	B	C	D	E	F	G	H	I	J	K	L	M
(i):	1	2	3	4	5	6	7	8	9	10	11	12	13
(ii):	3	6	9	12	15	18	21	24	27	30	33	36	39
Residue:	3	6	9	12	15	18	21	24	1	4	7	10	13
(iii):	C	F	I	L	O	R	U	X	A	D	G	J	M

Plain:	N	O	P	Q	R	S	T	U	V	W	X	Y	Z
(i):	14	15	16	17	18	19	20	21	22	23	24	25	26
(ii):	42	45	48	51	54	57	60	63	66	69	72	75	78
Residue:	16	19	22	25	2	5	8	11	14	17	20	23	26
(iii):	P	S	V	Y	B	E	H	K	N	Q	T	W	Z

The utilizable substitution alphabet which results is

```
Plain:  A B C D E F G H I J K L M N O P Q R S T U V W X Y Z
Cipher: C F I L O R U X A D G J M P S V Y B E H K N Q T W Z
```

By the same kind of procedure, a substitution alphabet can be constructed by using as a multiplier any odd key number (with the exception of a multiple of 13).

Let us examine the alphabet resulting from multiplication by 3 by looking at it in a different sort of way. Since the numerical values of the letters in the normal alphabet are consecutive and since we have been multiplying by 3, the numerical equivalents in the cipher sequence advance by 3's. In other words, we can derive the cipher sequence from the plain sequence by taking every third letter. Thus if we start the cipher sequence as above with the letter C, the next letter will be three beyond C, or F; then three beyond F gives I; three beyond I is L, etc. When we reach the letter X in this process, the next one three beyond it would be A, then D, $\cdots$. The continuation of this process produces the complete cipher sequence. Such a procedure of taking letters at constant intervals in a sequence is called *decimation*; the alphabet derived by using a decimated sequence as the cipher sequence is called a *decimated alphabet*. The process of decimation at an interval is equivalent to multiplication by the number corresponding to that interval.

It is of interest to note that the reversed standard alphabet used in the Army Cipher Disc (page 11) is a decimation of the normal alphabet. It corresponds to the multiplier 25 (or its equivalent, -1).

The multiplication process now provides us with a different type of general system from that of the direct standard alphabet. The key number assigned to any particular message permits the construction of a substitution alphabet by the above process of multiplication, and with this alphabet the processes of encipherment and decipherment can be performed.

Exercises

11. Solve the congruences

   (a) $4y + 2 \equiv 2y + 5 \pmod{17}$,   (b) $6x \equiv 3 \pmod 9$.

12. Find the reciprocal of 5 modulo 7.

13. What numbers have no reciprocal modulo 6? modulo n?

14. (a) The letters U, B, I, P are consecutive in the decimation of a normal sequence. What is the interval of decimation?
(b) With this interval as multiplier, construct the substitution alphabet.
(c) Can you use it to decipher the following message?

AVBIV KC DIGXITC PKVCJ FGE

1.7 Solution of decimated standard alphabets

How does a cryptanalyst cope with a message enciphered by means of a decimated alphabet? Here is a cipher message which we should like to solve.

VNY BYRVEIWR BLYDYLQ VNEV OWRQOLSBVSWRQ TALSRI
VNY RYPV VNLYY MWRVNQ JY METY SR VNY EIY JLEOCYVQ
RSRYVYYR VW VKYRVU WRY

As a first step we make a frequency distribution of the cipher letters.

A B C D E F G H I J K L M N O P Q R S T U V W X Y Z

The resulting pattern of frequencies does not seem to fit that of a direct standard alphabet. If we slide this distribution against that of the normal alphabet, we may find positions where individual high frequencies are matched with high frequencies, but for other letters the match will be quite poor. There is no position in which the overall match of the two distributions is good. We must conclude that the system is not one of a direct standard alphabet.

One possible manner of proceeding is to attempt to identify some of the letters. We could guess, for example, that Y_c, the most frequent letter, is probably E_p. And either V_c or R_c might be T_p.

To see how good these guesses are, we look at the places where those letters occur in the cipher text. We note the cipher word VNY occurring three times. If V_c is T_p and Y_c is E_p, then VNY is undoubtedly the word THE. That looks good! This plain language word seems to provide reasonably certain identification of three cipher letters. Let us write out the numerical equivalents of these plain and cipher letters:

	Plain	Cipher
T	20	22
H	8	14
E	5	25

If the general system is one of multiplication, we would expect that the three congruences

$$20k \equiv 22 \ (\text{mod } 26)$$
$$8k \equiv 14 \ (\text{mod } 26)$$
$$5k \equiv 25 \ (\text{mod } 26)$$

are consistent, and that their common solution for k is the multiplier we are seeking. In the first two congruences, the numbers 20 and 8 have the factor 2 in common with 26. These congruences, therefore, are satisfied by more than one value of k. But the third congruence has only one solution since 5 and 26 have no common factors. The solution is evidently $k = 5$.

If we substitute 5 for k in the first two congruences, we get

$$20(5) \equiv 100 \ (\text{mod } 26) \equiv 22 \ (\text{mod } 26)$$
$$8(5) \equiv 40 \ (\text{mod } 26) \equiv 14 \ (\text{mod } 26)$$

and this confirms the identification of T_p and H_p. Thus $k = 5$ is a solution in each case. It seems likely that the substitution alphabet was generated by decimation and that 5 was used as a multiplier. If we construct that alphabet and use it for decipherment, we find that it is correct, and that it produces the plain language of the original message.

The method just presented was the simplest way to solve the given cipher message. It was based on guessing some plain text and then assuming that the general system used a decimated sequence. We proceed now to attack the same problem in a different way which makes no assumptions and which is based on working solely with the frequency distribution.

We have already checked the frequency distribution of the cipher message against the distribution of the normal alphabet and have found that the two distributions cannot be made to match by sliding one against the other. This convinces us that the general system was not a direct standard alphabet and that, in the correct substitution alphabet, consecutive letters of the plain sequence are probably replaced by letters that are not consecutive in the normal alphabet. Perhaps a match between the cipher distribution and the normal distribution may be developed in some other way. Perhaps some systematic rearrangement of the cipher letters based on their frequencies might permit the determination of their order in the cipher sequence. This might then make possible the reconstruction of the substitution alphabet.

The best way to seek such a rearrangement is to try to discover some of the pairs of cipher letters which are the equivalents of consecutive plain language letters. We recall that in the normal frequency distribution the letters of high frequency include the pair N, O and the triplet R, S, T. The letters of low frequency include the pair J, K and the string U, V, W, X, Y, Z. Because of this consecutive grouping of a string of low frequency letters, we look at the low frequencies first. We take our cipher distribution and put a mark over every cipher letter that occurs infrequently—say, not more than once. (This is, of course, a statistical consideration and not every letter we are interested in will be examined by this procedure. If there are some unusual words in the message, a letter which they contain but which is normally very low in frequency may appear a few times. Conversely, one or more letters normally of higher frequency may appear infrequently or perhaps even not at all in this particular message. Thus the letters we shall check may not be the precise set we are interested in—although, with good luck, most of them will belong to it.)

```
 *     *  *     *  *  *          *             *               *         *        *
 A  B  C  D  E  F  G  H  I  J  K  L  M  N  O  P  Q  R  S  T  U  V  W  X  Y  Z
 _  =  _  _  ╪     ╪        =  =  _  ╪  =  ╪  =  _  ╪  ╪  ╪  =  _  ╪  ╪     ╪
                            _     _           ╪           ╪  _        ╪
                                              =           ╪           ╪
                                                                      ╪
                                                                      =
```

We examine the marks to see whether the letters we have picked out
appear in any kind of systematic positioning. And the first thing we
notice is that K, P, U, Z are evenly spaced—five letters apart.
If we go back 5 from K we reach F; five places in front of F is A,.
and all six of these letters are checked. Additionally, X, C and H
are five spaces apart. The string of letters A, F, K, P, U, Z fits the
picture of the infrequent letters U through Z in the normal alphabet.
The string X, C, H may include J, K, although the third letter is
a matter of concern. The triplet would probably not be I, J, K. It
might conceivably represent J, K, L. There is enough evidence in the
long string of letters to suggest that we may be dealing with a decimated alphabet. It isn't really necessary to seek further confirmation
before testing the idea of decimation, but it is interesting to observe
that among the high frequency letters, R and W are 5 apart, as
are L, Q, V; the former suggest the plain letters N, O, the latter
suggest R, S, T.

These facts prompt us then to examine what happens if we decimate
our cipher sequence on an interval of 5. Starting with A we construct
a sequence in which each letter is 5 places beyond its predecessor in
the normal alphabet. As we do this we carry with each letter the
indication of its cipher frequency as shown in our monographic
frequency distribution.

```
A  F  K  P  U  Z  E  J  O  T  Y  D  I  N  S  X  C  H  M  R  W  B  G  L  Q  V
-  -- -  -           ≠  =  =  =  ≠  -  =  ≠  ≠     -     =  ≠  ≠  =     ≠  ≠  ≠
                     ≠           -                    ≠  -        -     ≠
                     ≠                                =              ≠
                     =
```

Now we see the general appearance of a normal alphabet in the
characteristic pattern of high and low frequency letters. In addition
to the sets of letters mentioned in the previous paragraph, we see
the A, E, I pattern in the letters E, Y, S. As final confirmation we
set this distribution against the normal distribution and find an
excellent match when we set $A_p = E_c$. In this matching position,
we have reconstructed the substitution alphabet

```
Plain   A B C D E F G H I J K L M N O P Q R S T U V W X Y Z
Cipher  E J O T Y D I N S X C H M R W B G L Q V A F K P U Z
```

and it permits us to decipher the entire message. Its text is:

THE PENTAGON PREFERS THAT CONSCRIPTIONS DURING
THE NEXT THREE MONTHS BE MADE IN THE AGE BRACKETS
NINETEEN TO TWENTY ONE.

Note that the cipher string X C H represents the plain string
J K L and that L does not occur in the plain text.

Exercises

Solve the following messages:

15. SPSV CV XTS MIXTSMIXCAID OACSVASO EGF NFCVACNID
    CVOXFGMSVXO XE JCOAEPSF XTS XFGXT IFS CVJGAXCEV IVJ
    IVIDEKQ

16. SV SQ VNY OWMMWR KWRTYL WD EHH MYR NWK EMWRI QW MERU
    MSHHSWRQ WD DEOYQ VNYLY QNWAHT JY RWRY EHSCY

1.8 Monoalphabets based on linear transformations

Suppose the two ideas which have been described for a general
system, viz. shifting the alphabet, and multiplying by a constant,
are combined. For example, suppose we take the *cipher* sequence of
the Caesar alphabet and multiply each letter by 5.

Plain:	A	B	C	D	E	F	G	H	I	J	K	L	M
Num. Equiv.:	1	2	3	4	5	6	7	8	9	10	11	12	13
C_1 (Add 3):	4	5	6	7	8	9	10	11	12	13	14	15	16
Mult. by 5:	20	25	30	35	40	45	50	55	60	65	70	75	80
Residue:	20	25	4	9	14	19	24	3	8	13	18	23	2
C_2:	T	Y	D	I	N	S	X	C	H	M	R	W	B

Plain:	N	O	P	Q	R	S	T	U	V	W	X	Y	Z
Num. Equiv.:	14	15	16	17	18	19	20	21	22	23	24	25	26
C_1 (Add 3):	17	18	19	20	21	22	23	24	25	26	1	2	3
Mult. by 5:	85	90	95	100	105	110	115	120	125	130	5	10	15
Residue:	7	12	17	22	1	6	11	16	21	26	5	10	15
C_2:	G	L	Q	V	A	F	K	P	U	Z	E	J	O

Then the substitution alphabet which has C_2 as its cipher sequence will correspond to the relation $C = 5(P + 3)$ or $C = 5P + 15$, where C stands for the numerical equivalent of the cipher letter and P for that of the plain letter.

This substitution alphabet can, of course, be created in one step, instead of two, by performing the calculation $5P + 15$ on each plain letter.

A relation such as

$$C = aP + b$$

where a and b are constants is known as a *linear transformation* because the variables C and P are connected by a linear relationship, one involving only the first powers of the variables.

The two systems already studied, a shift and multiplication by a constant, are special cases of linear transformations. In the case of the direct standard alphabet a is 1, so that the linear relation reduces to $C = P + b$; b is the amount by which a plain letter is shifted to yield the cipher letter modulo 26. In the case of decimation b is zero, so that the relation reduces to $C = aP$; a is the multiplier yielding the decimation.

If two correspondents were to agree on the use of a general linear transformation, they would devise a means of associating two numbers with each message. These numbers, a and b, would determine the linear relation $C = aP + b$ with which the substitution alphabet could be generated.

Let us consider now the solution of a cipher message which, we assume, was written by using a cipher alphabet derived from the normal alphabet by a linear transformation. Then a method of attack is to identify the plain language equivalents of some of the cipher letters. Each plain-cipher equivalent provides a linear congruence, and with these congruences we need to determine two unknowns, the constants a and b of the linear transformation. Thus it may happen that just two identified letters suffice to yield a solution. Letter frequencies and guesses at plain language words are our tools in attempting to make such identifications.

Suppose we have the message:

GYOMXNOGNG QUGN ETNMX MPLMZOMXYM K TMMJOXA XEN
TKZ ZMQEBMF TZEQ KJKZQ EX YEXNMQLJKNOXA NHM TJEEF
ET XMI CXEIJMFAM IHOYH MKYH WMKZ RZOXAG IONH ON

The frequency distribution for this message is:

A B C D E F G H I J K L M N O P Q R S T U V W X Y Z

If we assume that the most frequent letter $M_c = E_p$, and that one
of the cipher letters E, N, O, X is T_p, it then seems likely that the
cipher NHM is THE. This tentative identification of the three letters

Cipher	Numerical Equivalent	Plain	Numerical Equivalent
N	14	T	20
H	8	H	8
M	13	E	5

gives rise to three congruences involving their numerical equivalents.
Each is obtained by substituting the numerical equivalents of the
identified letters into the congruence

$$C \equiv aP + b \pmod{26},$$

where a and b are the multiplier and shift, respectively. We obtain

$$14 \equiv 20a + b \pmod{26},$$
$$8 \equiv 8a + b \pmod{26},$$
$$13 \equiv 5a + b \pmod{26}.$$

If we subtract the third from the second congruence, we obtain

$$3a \equiv -5 \equiv 21 \pmod{26},$$
$$a = 7.$$

We use this value of a in the third congruence to find b:

$$35 + b \equiv 13 \pmod{26},$$
$$b \equiv -22 \equiv 4 \pmod{26},$$
$$b = 4.$$

The solution for a and b was obtained without using the congruence

$$14 \equiv 20a + b \pmod{26}.$$

It is found to satisfy that additional congruence, since

$$20(7) + 4 \equiv 144 \equiv 14 \pmod{26}.$$

The following substitution alphabet is generated by

$$C = 7P + 4:$$

```
Plain    A B C D E F G H I J K L M N O P Q R S T U V W X Y Z
Cipher   K R Y F M T A H O V C J Q X E L S Z G N U B I P W D
```

With this alphabet we are able to decipher the message. Its plain language text is

```
SCIENTISTS MUST OFTEN EXPERIENCE A FEELING NOT
FAR REMOVED FROM ALARM ON CONTEMPLATING THE FLOOD
OF NEW KNOWLEDGE WHICH EACH YEAR BRINGS WITH IT
```

The reader should verify that this same result can be obtained by working with the frequency distribution, as in the previous example. By marking off the low frequency letters and testing possible intervals between them, it is found that the interval 7 looks most promising. The following groups are found at interval 7: V, C; U, B; P, W, D. And, since the interval from B to P is 14, we can combine the latter two sets into one grouping:

$$U, B, -, P, W, D$$

This now corresponds to the set of plain language letters U to Z with W_p omitted.

If we decimate the alphabet on an interval of 7, carrying along the frequencies from our distribution (as we did on page 31), the new sequence matches the normal at the position $A_p = K_c$. This then provides the substitution alphabet derived above, and the message can be deciphered.

When the plain text is reconstructed, the reason for the blank in the sequence U, B, —, P, W, D is seen in the fact that the plain letter W occurs four times in the message, and therefore was not treated as a low frequency letter.

Exercises

17. Solve the congruences

   (a) $3x + 7 \equiv 9$ (mod 11)   (c) $2x + 1 \equiv 9x - 4$ (mod 23)
   (b) $4y + 6 \equiv 0$ (mod 13)

18. Solve the congruences

   (a) $3x \equiv 6$ (mod 9)   (b) $5x - 1 \equiv 3x + 1$ (mod 26)

19. Find the reciprocal of

   (a) 7 (mod 17)   (b) 9 (mod 26)   (c) 3 (mod 31)

Solve the following cryptograms:

20. JDI HVANGNKFKJS JDGJ EI MGS PGKF KT G EAVJDS UGQCI KC
    TAJ CQPPKUKITJ RQCJKPKUGJKAT PAV AQV VIPQCKTW JA CQHHAVJ
    KJ

21. MZ WZOGZWWJ GS EIZEWJZWN ZIB IZHU CGBX BXW NWSGOZ IF
    MRRMJMBKS VKB CGBX GBS IRWJMBGIZ VU XKQMZ VWGZOS

22. PU AOL AOLVYF VM UBTILYZ PA OHWWLUZ YHAOLY MYLXBLUASF
    AOHA IF ZVTL BULEWLJALK SBJR AOL TVZA LSLNHUA ULD AYBAOZ
    ZWYPUN BW IF PUKBJAPVU

23. R FX SNO FGYFRQ NG ONXNYYNZ GNY R WFEL TLLS PLTOLYQFP
    FSQ R CNEL ONQFP

24. Z UZMZGRX RH Z KVIHLM DSL RH SRTSOB VMGSFHRZHGRX ZYLFG
    HLNVGSRMT RM DSRXS BLF ZIV MLG VEVM IVNLGVOB RMGVIVHGVW

25. LE ULK LMC KZIE WZ LWC DWPE EFVERWEZIET NLE HKQ KP
    CIWEZNWPWI IREMNWKZ UWDD ZEJER PKRAEN WN LE UWDD XE
    DKZAWZA NK REZEU WN

26. BDSTGC WXHIDGN AXZT P STPU BPC PCHLTGH FJTHIXDCH CD DCT
    PHZTS

27. AH TNA PEPC UPBNTP DCPNQ HC DHHI PSBPOQ QKCHXDK TNAZ NAI
    DCPNQ TRJQNFPJ

CHAPTER TWO

General Monoalphabetic Substitution

2.1 Mixed alphabets

We have seen in the first chapter that a substitution alphabet derived by a linear transformation on the normal sequence introduces at most two unknown quantities: one determining the decimation interval, i.e. the alphabetic interval between successive letters of the cipher sequence, and the second the number of positions of shift of the cipher sequence against the plain sequence. To solve a cryptogram which has been produced in such a way, it is usually sufficient to find just two correct plain-cipher equivalents. For, if we know that the cipher letters whose numerical equivalents are C_1 and C_2 correspond to plain sequence letters with numerical equivalents P_1 and P_2, we can construct two congruences

$$C_1 \equiv aP_1 + b \ (\text{mod } 26), \qquad a = \text{decimation interval},$$
$$C_2 \equiv aP_2 + b \ (\text{mod } 26), \qquad b = \text{amount of shift},$$

whose solution yields the values of a and b. (In some instances, there might be ambiguities, as when a congruence has more than one solution, but such a situation only requires trying the different possible answers to see which one will yield plain language.) If the cryptanalyst could determine the plain language equivalents of a larger number of letters or of a whole word, he would be provided with a greater number of plain-cipher equivalents and these would

37

then ensure that there are no ambiguities in the solution of the key numbers.

Thus it appears that the person desiring security should design his substitution alphabet in a more complicated way than by the use of a linear relationship. If the substitution alphabet is constructed in such a way that the knowledge of some plain-cipher equivalents does not yield information about other plain-cipher equivalents, the reconstruction of the substitution alphabet would become much more difficult. For example, the cipher sequence could be derived by a random selection of the letters of the alphabet. As one illustration, imagine the 26 letters of the alphabet written on pieces of paper, placed in a hat, thoroughly mixed and then picked out one at a time. The sequence of selecting the letters results in a substitution alphabet in which each plain-cipher equivalence is independent of the others. An example of such an alphabet, called a *random alphabet* is the following:

```
Plain:   A B C D E F G H I J K L M N O P Q R S T U V W X Y Z
Cipher:  Q N T L R A X U G C P K B Z F I V D H M O W E Y S J
```

Most of the cryptographic problems encountered in magazines and newspapers use randomly generated alphabets. A disadvantage of such alphabets, from the point of view of communications, is the difficulty of committing the cipher sequence to memory. If the sequence has to be written out, there is the danger that it may be lost or stolen. This suggests the idea of generating a cipher sequence in some systematic way which will make it easy to construct the sequence and yet create a sufficient amount of mixing to gain most of the advantages of randomness. Many ingenious schemes have been devised for deriving such sequences; the reader can no doubt think up some of his own. Two of the most commonly used methods will be briefly described as illustrations.

The first method produces what is called a *keyword mixed sequence*. The cryptographer is required to remember just one important word—the keyword. Suppose, by way of example, that the key word is DEMOCRATIC. The first step in constructing the sequence is to write out the keyword, letter by letter, omitting any repeated letters. If we do this with the word DEMOCRATIC, we get DEMO-CRATI; the last C is omitted because a C has already occurred in the 5th position. The cipher sequence is then completed by writing the remaining letters of the alphabet in their normal order. If we do this in our example, we obtain the cipher sequence

D E M O C R A T I B F G H J K L N P Q S U V W X Y Z

The substitution alphabet is now obtained by writing the cipher sequence under a normal plain sequence. There would, of course, have to be agreement about the positioning of the sequences against one another. This can be accomplished by the specification of one plain-cipher pair. A common arrangement is for the first letter of the keyword to be written under A of the plain sequence. In the case of our example, we would have $A_p = D_c$.

```
Plain:  A B C D E F G H I J K L M N O P Q R S T U V W X Y Z
Cipher: D E M O C R A T I B F G H J K L N P Q S U V W X Y Z
```

If such a substitution alphabet is used for enciphering a message, the cryptanalyst who attempts to solve it must determine enough plain-cipher equivalents to find the keyword before he can reconstruct the entire sequence.

If it is felt that this process does not create a sufficient amount of mixing, the following modification can be made. After writing the keyword without repeated letters, we write the remaining letters of the alphabet on successive lines under the keyword:

```
                D E M O C R A T I
                B F G H J K L N P
                Q S U V W X Y Z
```

Then, the letters are read vertically in the manner known as *columnar transposition*: column 1 is followed by column 2, then by column 3, etc., yielding the mixed sequence:

D B Q E F S M G U O H V C J W R K X A L Y T N Z I P

This cipher sequence, to which we shall refer as a *transposed keyword mixed sequence*, has most of the advantages of one derived by a completely random process, yet can be systematically constructed from one previously-agreed-upon keyword.

One slight disadvantage of using such a mixed sequence becomes apparent in the process of decipherment, but can easily be overcome. If the substitution alphabet

```
Plain:   A B C D E F G H I J K L M N O P Q R S T U V W X Y Z
Cipher:  D B Q E F S M G U O H V C J W R K X A L Y T N Z I P
```

is being used to decipher a message, it is necessary to search around in
the cipher sequence to find the letter being deciphered. To eliminate
this bother, the alphabet can be rearranged so that the cipher letters
are in order. As each cipher letter is placed in its alphabetic position,
its corresponding plain letter is moved with it. Such a rearrangement
of the substitution alphabet above yields

```
Plain:   S B M A D E H K Y N Q T G W J Z C P F V I L O R U X
Cipher:  A B C D E F G H I J K L M N O P Q R S T U V W X Y Z
```

In this form (or with the modification that the cipher sequence is
written above the plain sequence), the substitution alphabet is called
a *deciphering alphabet* as contrasted to the *enciphering alphabet*, which
has the plain sequence in normal order. The two forms give, of course,
the same substitution alphabet. They point up the fact that a mixed
alphabet can be obtained by scrambling either the plain sequence or
the cipher sequence.

Exercise

28. Determine the keywords used to develop the following mixed sequences.
    (The dots stand for unknown letters.) Note that the first two sequences
    end so as to indicate that there has been no columnar transposition.

    (a)   S E C R T M A G B D F H I J K L N O P Q U V W X Y Z

    (b)   U N I T E D A O S B C F G H J K L M P Q R V W X Y Z

    (c)   U B M Y N C O Z I F P T G Q E H R D J V S K W A L X

    (d)   W A H . Y I B J Q Z R . K T E D . . L F N V S G O X

    (e)   N A U E B V W C X . D Z O F R G . H T J I L M . S Q

2.2   Solution of mixed alphabet ciphers

We proceed now to study the cryptanalysis of a message enciphered
with a mixed alphabet. And again, by way of illustration, we take an

example to assist in developing the necessary ideas. The message is the following:

```
UZ QSO VUOHXMOPV GPOZPEVSG ZWSZ OPFPESX UDBMETSX AIZ
VUEPHZ HMDZSHZO WSFP APPD TSVP QUZW YMXUZUHSX
EPYEPOPDZSZUFPO MB ZWP FUPZ HMDJ UD TMOHMQ
```

As a first step in trying to solve this problem, we make a monographic distribution.

If we try to match the normal frequency distribution against it, we find no position in which the distributions match one another. Nor do we have any success in trying to convert this unknown distribution to the normal by decimation. The conclusion from these facts is that the cipher was not arrived at by a linear transformation. The substitution alphabet must be mixed.

In order to solve a cipher based on a mixed substitution alphabet it is necessary to determine the plain text equivalents of some of the cipher letters and thereby decipher one or more words of the original plain text. If such an entry can be made into the original message, it normally proves sufficient to permit reconstruction of the complete text. Techniques for affecting such an entry into the message are based on properties of language, on the way letters combine with one another to form words in English. They fall under three major headings.

The first aid in the cryptanalysis of a message like the one we are trying to solve is the frequency of occurrence of individual letters. From the monographic distribution which we have already made, we can distinguish certain letters as being of high frequency, others of medium frequency, etc. This information alone may not be sufficient to provide any firm identifications, especially if the message is not very long. In general, it only suggests that certain cipher letters probably correspond to plain language letters belonging to a limited set. In our problem, for example, it seems possible that P_c and Z_c may be the equivalents of E_p and T_p, but even if that is so, there is still a question as to which is equivalent to which. The letters H_c, M_c, O_c, S_c, U_c, all of high frequency, probably correspond to plain letters from the set {A, I, N, O, R, S}. And most of the low frequency letters A_c, B_c, I_c, J_c, Q_c, T_c, Y_c are likely to be deciphered by letters from the set {G, J, K, Q, V, W, X, Y, Z}.

The information deducible from monographic frequencies can be supplemented by information about word beginnings and endings. In a study of over 16,000 words of newspaper text the ten most frequent initial and final letters were found to be:

Initial	No. of words	Final	No. of words
T	2,614	E	3,325
A	1,802	S	2,077
S	1,213	D	1,649
O	1,176	N	1,592
I	922	T	1,587
C	918	R	906
W	833	Y	903
P	768	F	745
B	757	O	744
F	666	L	599

Let us apply these data to figure out how to pair off P_c and Z_c with their probable equivalents E_p and T_p. In our message Z_c is both a frequent initial and final letter; P_c occurs frequently as a final but not at all as an initial. Hence, Z_c seems more likely than P_c to be T_p.

Each of the infrequent letters Q_c and T_c begins two words. Their equivalents are likely to be found in the set {C, W, P, B, F} of infrequent letters which often begin words.

In general, the use of monographic frequencies and frequencies of initial and final letters may suggest a set of possible equivalents for some of the cipher letters. We don't usually expect to obtain more precise information about plain language equivalents from frequency considerations alone.

The next main technique in solving a monoalphabet is to try to distinguish vowels from consonants. An important tool for this purpose is the study of short words, say of two, three, or four letters. We know that each such word must contain a vowel. It might be possible to determine from these short words that certain cipher letters represent vowels. Such information will prove a great aid in obtaining the solution. Thus in our message we note the 2-letter words UZ, MB, UD. From the word MB we conclude that either M_c or B_c is a vowel, and since B_c is so infrequent it seems more likely that M_c is a vowel, unless, perhaps, $B_c = Y_p$. From the words UZ and UD, we would conclude that either U_c is a vowel or that both Z_c and D_c are vowels. In the latter case, U_c would be a consonant. If U_c is a consonant, what possible plain language words could UZ and UD be? They could be ME and MY, or BE and BY and these seem to be about the only possibilities. They are not very likely since U_c seems much too frequent to correspond to either B_p or M_p.

It seems probable then that U_c is a vowel, Z_c and D_c are consonants. If Z_c is a consonant, then the word ZWP would suggest that either W_c or P_c is a vowel. The facts already developed about P_c and Z_c from frequency considerations would then make P_c the likely vowel in ZWP.

The third technique we utilize is that of "pattern words". There are many instances of words which have repeated letters in them with a distinctive pattern of repetition. This pattern will, of course, be apparent in the cipher since the substitution procedure replaces all occurrences of a plain-text letter by the same cipher equivalent. By way of example, words like BEGINNING, COMMITTEE, PEOPLE, TOMORROW, DIVISION, NONSENSE can often be recognized from the positioning of their repeated letters, particularly if the frequency information confirms the relative frequencies of the letters in them, or knowledge of vowels and consonants is consistent with the word. With practice and experience, one learns to recognize many patterned words. Compilations have been published of collections of word patterns arranged so as to make it possible to hunt up words according to the pattern which their encipherment presents. A particular point in this regard is the fact that special circumstances connected with a message sometimes give indications of its general subject matter. A message might be suspected to contain a specific word, like the name of an individual or a place or some commodity, that has a characteristic repetition pattern in its spelling. If the message includes such a word, the pattern would make it possible to locate it by the recognition of its repeated letters.

It isn't necessary for utilizable pattern words to be long. Words like THAT, WHICH, WHERE can at times be identified on the basis of their repeated letters. Even the absence of pattern can be of assistance. Thus a very long word with no repeated letter at all—in conjunction with the frequencies of the letters contained in it—may be found to have only one likely decipherment.

Further, patterns need not be restricted to single words. Such phrases as FROM TIME TO TIME, AS SOON AS, ON ACCOUNT OF can be readily recognized. The identification in a cipher message of just one word, or phrase, or even of a few individual letters may provide the crucial entry which will suffice to reconstruct the entire message.

Let us see how these ideas can be applied to our problem. Having assumed that U_c is a vowel and Z_c is a consonant (probably T_p), we note the word ZWSZ which looks like THAT. If this assumption is correct, then ZWP could be the very common word THE and

```
        WSFP   APPD

        h..e   .ee.
```

suggests the words HAVE BEEN.

If we insert these words in the message and then replace each cipher letter that appears in them (i.e., each tentatively identified cipher letter) by its plain letter equivalent everywhere in the cipher message, we obtain

```
UZ QSO VUOHXMOPV GPOZPEVSG ZWSZ OPFPESX UDBMETSX AIZ
t  a             e   e te  a that eve a   n       a b t

VUEPHZ HMDZSHZO WSFP APPD TSVP QUZW YMXUZUHSX
  e t   nta t   have been a e   th       t  a

EPYEPOPDZSZUFPO MB ZWP FUPZ HMDJ UD TMOHMQ
e  e e tat ve      the v et   n    n
```

It now follows that the first plain word is either AT or IT. But A_p has already been determined as S_c. Thus $U_c = I_p$.

With this new letter identified, it would appear that the cipher word QUZW is WITH and the value W_p for Q_c then suggests that the second word should be WAS. These suggested equivalents

I_p, W_p, S_p for U_c, Q_c, and O_c, respectively, have appropriate frequencies. They indicate that I_p and S_p are high frequency letters, as they should be, and W_p has low frequency. The message now appears as follows:

```
UZ QSO VUOHXMOPV GPOZPEVSG ZWSZ OPFPESX UDBMETSX AIZ
it was is   se    este   a   that seve a  in     a b t

VUEPHZ HMDZSHZO WSFP APPD TSVP QUZW YMXUZUHSX
 i e t   nta ts have been a e with    iti a

EPYEPOPDZSZUFPO MB ZWP FUPZ HMDJ UD TMOHMQ
 e  esentatives    the viet   n    n   s w
```

The combinations of letters produced so far look very good indeed, and we might be able to make some pretty good guesses at a few of the words which are almost completely filled in. For example, the words YESTERDAY, SEVERAL, REPRESENTATIVES, all have recognizable patterns which might be checked. The words VIET CONG seem to stand out at the end of the message.

Alternatively, aware that the high frequency letters N_p, O_p, R_p have not yet been identified, we might try these plain letters in turn for the still unknown frequent cipher letters, and such a process would certainly result in further identifications. With only a little more work, the complete solution of the message would become available. Its text is:

```
IT WAS DISCLOSED YESTERDAY THAT SEVERAL INFORMAL BUT
DIRECT CONTACTS HAVE BEEN MADE WITH POLITICAL
REPRESENTATIVES OF THE VIET CONG IN MOSCOW
```

As a final step in the solution of this problem, it is desirable, if possible, to reconstruct the complete substitution alphabet, and to determine how it was devised. Such information may be valuable in deciphering other messages between the same correspondents. An understanding of their cryptographic procedures and habits may prove very useful.

The substitution alphabet derived from the message just solved is

```
Plain:  A B C D E F G H I J K L M N O P Q R S T U V W X Y Z
Cipher: S A H V P B J W U . . X T D M Y . E O Z I F Q . G .
```

The cipher sequence has some blank letters because the plain text message did not contain all 26 letters.

Note the letters V, W, X, Y, Z in the cipher sequence separated by a constant interval of four. If we write these letters down in a row, and if we then write above each the three letters which precede it in the cipher sequence, we get

```
S P U T .
A B . D E
H J . M O
V W X Y Z
```

The unused identified remainder of the cipher sequence is then added to the array by putting F and G on the second line to fill the gap between E and H:

```
S P U T . I .
A B . D E F G
H J . M O Q .
V W X Y Z
```

The hitherto unidentified letter C can be inserted between B and D. We see now that we have a vertically transposed keyword-mixed sequence. The keyword contains 7 letters of which 5 are known. A sixth must be N (missing between M and O), and the seventh is K or L. It seems highly probable that the keyword is SPUTNIK, in which case the complete cipher sequence can be reconstructed.

The above example illustrates how such a monoalphabetic cipher can often be solved. Clues from the relative frequencies of the cipher letters and from short words, combined with pattern information, make possible the determination of some of the equivalents. These are then entered wherever they appear in the message; additional identifications are suggested, and the text is gradually unraveled.

The solution of such problems is largely a matter of practice and experience. If the message is sufficiently long it proves only a question of time until an entry is obtained.

We will not pursue the solution of ciphers of this kind any further because the next topic to be introduced includes them as a special case.

Exercises

Solve the following cryptograms:

29. XTEIA DSL ASQA FKSF FKY IVYOPYUJQ NI PAY NI LNVRA TU
    SMYVTJSU UYLAESEYV YUCDTAK SUR FKYTV VSUG NVRYV SVY
    JDNAYDQ VYDSFYR

30. HCB RWOEUWY NXHY QM QWIUFOKBN SQLOBHY OS HQ BFPUWIB HCB
    POTBS UFN OFLWBUSB HCB SHUFNUWN QM POTOFI QM UPP HCB
    RBQRPB

2.3 Solution of monoalphabets in five letter groupings

It is evident that a major aid to the solution of the previous example lay in the fact that the cipher text groups were the original
word lengths. It is the knowledge of word lengths—and the possible
use of patterns within them—that is essential in the solution of most
newspaper and magazine cryptograms. The situation would be quite
different if we had no knowledge of where words begin and end.
And, in fact, this is the next step in the improvement of cryptograms—
the elimination of word lengths.

Suppose that an enciphered message was written in uniform group-
ings of five letters. (This number is chosen because it is regularly
encountered in commercial communications and is the most commonly used grouping in cipher communications.) As an example,
consider the following message:

    MYTKI JIRUL AZOAH MIJAC UYGII JIUJA CHETR JMRUY MJFAG
    RMRPJ FTMEX ALAZU YMRQM OAZEX OAZRU ARTRI TGELG IJHAR
    JITJU AVYMO YVTLV IFMPY UXIOM XIUAP A

How might we solve it?

If we make a monographic frequency distribution, we have:

```
A B C D E F G H I J K L M N O P Q R S T U V W X Y Z
≠ = ≡ ≡ ≡ ≡ ≠ ≠ ˉ ≡ ≠   ≠ = ˉ ≠   ≠ ≠ =   ≡ ≠ ≡
≠       ≠ ≠   ≠       ≠       = ≡         =
≡       =     ˉ
```

This distribution does not yield to any attacks based on the assumption of a linear transformation.

By means of the monographic frequency distribution we can divide the cipher letters into groups of high, medium, and low frequency. We can then say, for example, that the high frequency cipher letters A, I, J, M, R, T, U, Y will probably have their plain language equivalents among the letters E, T, N, R, O, I, A, S.

We would like next to get some information about consonants and vowels, perhaps determine some cipher letters whose equivalents will be among the letters A, E, I, O or others whose equivalents will be among N, R, S, T. In the previous example we had the help of short words, each of which must contain a vowel. We are now denied that aid. However, we do have a similar aid in the knowledge that every syllable must contain a vowel. To take advantage of that fact we make use of information about the way letters combine with one another.

There is much more information derivable from language patterns than just the characteristic frequencies of the individual letters. Extensive counts have been made of digraphs (combinations of two letters) and trigraphs (combinations of three letters) in very large amounts of text. As in the case of monographic counts, these combinations occur with characteristic frequencies, which do not normally vary widely between samples. These characteristic frequencies are of importance in a number of cryptanalytic applications. For our present purposes, it will be sufficient to examine only some major features.

A count made on more than 80,000 characters of newspaper text produced the following numbers of occurrences for the 30 most frequent digraphs (the complete count is given in tabular form in Appendix A):

TH	2161	ED	890	OF	731
HE	2053	TE	872	IT	704
IN	1550	TI	865	AL	681
ER	1436	OR	861	AS	648
RE	1280	ST	823	HA	646
ON	1232	AR	764	NG	630
AN	1216	ND	761	CO	606
EN	1029	TO	756	SE	595
AT	1019	NT	743	ME	573
ES	917	IS	741	DE	572

Note that these 30 combinations, whose total number of occurrences is more than 28000, account for about one third of all the digraphs. Note further some of the properties of these digraphs. Twenty-five of the thirty digraphs contain one vowel. Included in these 25 are cases of reversals like ER, RE; ES, SE; ED, DE. Of the five combinations of two consonants, three contain T and three contain N. Not one of the entire set of high frequency digraphs is a vowel-vowel combination.

As a summary of the general information conveyed by this listing, we could say that:

1. Vowels tend to combine with consonants rather than with one another.

2. Letters present in a great variety of different digraphs are most probably vowels.

3. Consonants—with the exception of T and N—tend to combine most frequently with vowels.

4. If a digraph and its reversal both occur, one letter is likely to be a vowel.

From this same sample the following counts were obtained for the twelve most frequent trigraphs:

THE	1717	TER	232
AND	483	RES	219
TIO	384	ERE	212
ATI	287	CON	206
FOR	284	TED	187
THA	255	COM	185

The pattern of alternation of vowels and consonants continues to be evident.

How can we utilize this kind of information? To begin with, we must examine the digraphic frequencies in the message we are studying. To this end, we prepare a *trigraphic frequency distribution* by displaying, for each occurrence of a cipher letter, the letters immediately preceding and following it. From such a display, we shall be able to look at digraphs by considering the first and second and also the second and third letters of our triples.

The method of preparation is straightforward and is illustrated by the frequency study (p. 51) of the cipher message on p. 47 we are trying to solve. Each letter of the message is recorded in turn. It is listed, not by a tally mark, but by setting down the identities of the letter which precedes it and that which follows it. Thus the first letter M is listed as ·Y to show that it has no predecessor and is followed by Y. Then under Y we list MT to show that the letter Y is preceded by M and followed by T. Then under T we list YK and continue in this fashion throughout the entire message. The completed distribution tells us the frequency of each letter and the identities of all the letters preceding and following it. An added element of information is the occurrence of any trigraphic repetitions. These are indicated in the frequency distribution by underlines. The repeated trigraphs can be spotted in the process of making the distribution. They should be found and marked in the cipher message. At the same time they should be examined to see whether the repeated portions extend beyond the trigraph. They might disclose instances of entire words (or phrases) being repeated, an occurrence which could prove additionally helpful in trying to derive the plain text.

As a next step in solving our cryptogram, we try to distinguish vowels from consonants. Consider the high frequency cipher letters A, I, M, J, R, U, T, Y, and list the repeated digraphs involving these letters, together with the frequency of each digraph:

A	I	J	M	R	T	U	Y
0:3 Z:4	J:3 J:4	I:4 I:3	Y:3 R:3	M:3 U:3	I:2 R:2	R:3 Y:3	U:3 M:3
L:2 C:2	G:2 U:2	R:2 A:2	0:2	T:2 J:2		I:2 A:3	
J:2 R:2	X:2 T:2	F:2		A:2			
U:3							

This table indicates that the digraph OA occurs three times, AZ four times, etc.

The large number and variety of repeated digraphs containing A_c would suggest that A_c is a vowel; the frequently repeated reversed cipher digraphs JI, IJ, coupled with the occurrence of reversals RI, IR would indicate that I_c is a vowel, perhaps E_p. A kind of confirmation that A_c and I_c may both be vowels is the fact that there are no occurrences of AI or IA. Further J_c combines

A	B	C	D	E	F	G	H	I	J	K	L	M	N	O	P	Q	R	S	T	U	V	W	X	Y	Z
LZ	AU		HT		JA	YI	AM	KJ	II	TI	UA	.Y		ZA	RJ	RM	IU		YK	RL	AY		EA	MT	AO
OH	AH		MX		JT	AR	CE	JR	IA		AA	HI		MA	MY		TJ		ER	CY	YT		EO	UG	AU
JC			ZX		IM	TE	JA	MJ	II		EG	JR		XA	AA		MU		FM	IJ	LI		UI	UM	AE
JC			GL			LI		UA			TV	YJ		MY			GM		RR	RY			MI	UM	AR
FG								RM				RR		IM			MP		IG	ZY				VM	
XL								MF				TE					MQ		IJ	RA				OV	
LZ								PF				YR					ZU		VL	JA				PU	
OZ								IH				QO					AT			YX					
OZ								RI				YO					TI			IA					
UR								TU				FP					AJ								
HR								XO				OX													
UV								XU																	
UP																									
P.																									

frequently with both I_c and A_c. We make the assumption then that A_c and I_c are vowels, J_c is a consonant. From this it would follow that U_c is probably a consonant since it forms frequent digraphs with A_c and I_c.

A check on the vowel character of A_c and I_c is seen in the examination of low frequency letters, which are reasonably certain to be consonants, and the observation that they combine often with A_c and I_c. Since the diagraph II appears twice, I_c is probably neither A_p nor I_p. The reversed digraphs IJ, JI, and IR, RI, would make E_p a more likely candidate than O_p for I_c. What about M_c, the third highest letter in frequency? It combines not at all with A_c and only once with I_c. It might be a vowel since it combines so seldom with cipher letters we have tentatively decided to be vowels. M_c combines with low frequency letters like Q_c and P_c and H_c. Also M_c combines frequently with R_c which looks like a consonant because it combines with both A_c and I_c, with the latter in both directions.

Summarizing all these possibilities, we have:

M_c, A_c, I_c: probably vowels; $I_c = E_p$?
U_c, R_c, J_c: probably consonants; J_c is likely to be N_p, R_p, or S_p (because of reversed digraphs with I_c)

Since every syllable must have at least one vowel, a kind of check on the tentative identification of vowels is to examine their positioning throughout the message. Let us go through the message and indicate tentatively identified vowels:

```
MYTKI JIRUL AZOAH MIJAC UYGII JIUJA CHETR JMRUY MJFAG
 *   *   *     *  *  ** *     ** *  *          *   *  *

RMRPJ FTMEX ALAZU YMRQM OAZEX OAZRU ARTRI TGELG IJHAR
 *       *  ** *     *  *  *  *  *  *  *          *  *

JITJU AVYMO YVTLV IFMPY UXIOM XIUAP A
 *     *  *     ** *    ** *  ** *  *
```

The spacing looks good. There are only two places where vowels are adjacent and there are only four sequences of five or more letters that do not contain a vowel. It is not impossible to have that many consecutive consonants—in fact five consecutive consonants can be found in one single word (for example, STRENGTHS, EIGHTHS). But it is not very likely that all four sequences

C H E T R J,   R P J F T,   T G E L G,   O Y V T L V

are vowel free. Of the four frequent vowels A, E, I, O we presumably have three. Can we find in these sequences a cipher letter which could be the fourth vowel? It would seem reasonable that it is one of the set E_c, T_c, L_c, with T_c most likely since it occurs in all four sequences. E_c combines with M_c which we have assumed to be a vowel, and so E_c looks unlikely as a vowel. L_c occurs only four times and combines in both directions with the probable vowel A_c. T_c is therefore a more probable equivalent for a vowel.

We now have some information about most of the high frequency letters. What about the two letters U_c and R_c which we believe to be consonants? If one of these is T_p we might be able to identify it by looking for the frequent digraphs formed by T_p, in particular for TH, the most frequent digraph in plain language. R_c is followed three times by U_c, but U_c appears too frequently to be H_p. U_c is followed three times by Y_c which might possibly be H_p, and preceded three times by R_c which could be N_p or S_p.

The thing to do now is to examine portions of the text containing patterns we might fit words to, preferably portions which include several letters possibly identifiable on the basis of the above information, to see whether we might find an entering wedge through a useful guess of plain text.

We find some interesting patterns, e.g.:

O A Z E X O A Z
V Y M O Y V
U X I O M X I U
U Y G I I J I U J

In trying to guess words to fit any of these patterns we must simultaneously guess where words begin and end.

The last of these patterns contains high frequency letters only, some of which we have tentatively identified. If we insert the values we have, the text will read

$$\ldots \text{U Y G I I J I U J A C H} \ldots$$

$$\ldots \text{t.h . e e} \begin{Bmatrix} n \\ r \\ s \end{Bmatrix} \text{e t} \begin{Bmatrix} n \\ r \\ s \end{Bmatrix} \ldots \ldots$$

It looks as if G_c might be R_p to yield the word THREE. Then J_c has to be N_p or S_p.

$$\ldots \text{U Y G I I J I U J A C H} \ldots$$

$$\ldots \text{t h r e e} \begin{Bmatrix} n \\ s \end{Bmatrix} \text{e t} \begin{Bmatrix} n \\ s \end{Bmatrix} \ldots \ldots$$

Of these two, S_p looks much better since it yields the words THREE SETS. We seem to be on the trail of some text. Let us fill in the plain letters T, H, R, E, S wherever the corresponding cipher letters U, Y, G, I, J occur.

```
MYTKI JIRUL AZOAH MIJAC UYGII JIUJA CHETR JMRUY MJFAG
h     e se t         es    three sets         s th  s  r

RMRPJ FTMEX ALAZU YMRQM OAZEX OAZRU ARTRI TGELG IJHAR
s           t  h         t          e  r r es

JITJU AVYMO YVTLV IFMPY UXIOM XIUAP A
se st h     h     e     h t e   et
```

The combinations that appear look very good—there doesn't seem to be anything unacceptable about them. If these values are correct, we might try next to identify the vowels M_c, A_c, T_c whose equivalents should be A_p, I_p, O_p in some order. We also have an unidentified high frequency consonant R_c. Since we have already identified the plain letters T, R, S, R_c might be N_p, a possibility we had suspected when we were trying to determine T_p. Inserting this information in the portion of the text consisting of the eighth, ninth and tenth cipher groups, we find

$$\text{J M R U Y} \quad \text{M J F A G} \quad \text{R M R P J}$$

$$\text{s} \begin{Bmatrix} a \\ i \\ o \end{Bmatrix} \text{n t h} \begin{Bmatrix} a \\ i \\ o \end{Bmatrix} \text{s . . r n} \begin{Bmatrix} a \\ i \\ o \end{Bmatrix} \text{n . s}$$

Now if $M_c = I_p$, we read

$$\text{sinthis.} \begin{Bmatrix} o \\ a \end{Bmatrix} \text{rnin.s,}$$

which yields

in this mornings

The rest of the text can now be quickly determined. It is

```
I HAVE SENT YOU COPIES OF THREE SETS OF PLANS IN THIS
MORNINGS MAIL DO YOU THINK I COULD COUNT ON AN EARLY
RESPONSE AS TO WHICH WAY WE MIGHT DECIDE TO GO
```

It is suggested as an exercise that the reader determine the substitution alphabet and the keyword which generated it. (Note: Write the alphabet in enciphering form to find the keyword. A deciphering alphabet will not yield the desired information.)

The procedure just demonstrated shows that the solution of a monoalphabet can often be achieved using monographic and digraphic frequency distributions to distinguish vowels and consonants from among the high frequency letters and then, with this information, identifying some plain text on the basis of repetition patterns. Once a correct entry has been found by such a process, the completion of the problem normally follows without difficulty.

Exercises

Solve:

```
31. GJGNX BBWBJ LMGTX BGQCB ODBTL BXOGD VJGJB MWSUS LGXDO
    XGRLA SUUMC SQCXY UBTVY LRVXL CBIXB TBJLG JDUVL LBXDU
    SFBXG JOVWT BUBQL SVJTD TLBWL VOBLB XWSJB LCBVX OBXVR
    SJOYQ LSVJ

32. ETYOQ PYRFZ DIROD RSRRD LRHYP MYOFY TPSMF ISFRY BDFQS
    FDTOU DTFIY LRQFY POFSF YOSRP ESRSJ SISVY SBTYY PDRRY
    WFTYS FQYOB DVYTR QRBFI YHDRF TDCPY UYROY SRPRY LFTSC
    QFMDU FIYES RSJSH SRSC
```

2.4 Monoalphabets with symbols as cipher equivalents

Some remarks might be appropriate at this point about ciphers composed of symbols other than the letters of the alphabet. An interesting example, one of the first instances of cryptography occurring in literature, is in Edgar Allen Poe's story *The Gold Bug*. A widely used method of encipherment is known as the Pig-Pen Cipher. In one form, the letters A through I are represented in left to right order by the nine cells of the tic-tac-toe diagram.

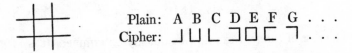

The letters J through R are these same cells with a single dot; S through Z are written with two dots. The word CRYPTOGRAPHY would be enciphered

If ciphers based on symbols are monoalphabetic (and they usually are), the methods of solution follow along the lines that have already been described. Actually, such a cipher becomes just like the kind we have been discussing if an arbitrary substitution is made of letters for the symbols in the cryptogram. Such a step, by introducing familiar characters, might make the problem easier to handle. However the cryptanalyst must keep in mind the fact that there may be some system of assigning values to the symbols which may no longer be evident if they are arbitrarily replaced by letters.

Exercises

Solve:

33.

```
·3  4  3 ·2 ·4      3  1  2  1    2 ·2  3  1  4  3  1 ·3 ·4  1· 2  3

3  1 ·2 ·2  1·  1 ·3    2  1 ·2 ·4  4  1 ·2    ·4  4  1  2    ·4  4  1 ·4

1 ·3  1· 2  3    ·2  1  3  1  4·  1 ·2    3  1  2  1 ·3    1· ·4     1· ·3

1 ·3  1  4    2  1:    1  1  1 ·4  1  1 ·2 ·3    1  2  4    1· 2

2 ·2  1 ·1  1  1  2  3  1:    1  3  4  1  4·  1 ·4  1· 3  2    1  2  4

2  3 ·2    ·4 ·3  1  2 ·3  3  3  1  1  2  1· 3    ·4  1  4·  1  4  4  3  2  1:
```

34. 15 "&& *(@ .*"/. *(@ .–% ;· %@"/@.* *! *(@
     @"/*("%'   ;*   ;·   *(@ 2@%*@/ !5 *(@ .!&"/ .$.*@3
     "&& *(@ ,&"%@*· 3!:@ "/!–%' ;*

35.

Solve the following cryptograms:

36. JTLR RQ VJQFIJU FCTJ RQ KTIYT HJ QWWQERXJIRS RCT DQKR
    IDWQERHJR RCIJU IJ MIZT IK RQ VJQF FCTJ RQ ZQETUQ HJ
    HONHJRHUT

37. MOOGA NBOIF HBIPN FIHFM OOIAL CKNRY NTVYN YQIVZ IFBRV
    PNTCA NTVVZ IFVNR PZMVZ LHVOI VLFLY OKMTY LVGAL PSHKN
    RQAMH GLVBN OYOKM TYLVH HGLTI HPARF BOI

38. KDBEW IKUET WXKPG KKBQD GUQPV HBCBV WTEBG KLDUQ DDPIP
    IIUIK BHUGK DBAUX KDWRQ WEEYG UQPKU WGKDB WXSUI KDPKW
    RKBVB OXPTD S

39. RFDIM ERDLM BREOM KKDYI QERGY OIMYE JROLB GQDHD YRDLB
    KOVED RQDKO JIREO MYOML DTMEM UEKQB DJBML YBJJE MUZOQ
    BPIJJ ABYSO ZEKQB DJERQ OOPKZ QOTBQ BARDQ QEROQ G

40. NXRPC GACPU RFCAW UVFSW QWRXU OBXVW AQXVF KRFWP KRTCK
    XWARF SVFKD CFCLO VXEGK VPECZ PDWFS COCGK CXAWO BYKUV
    GGCGL CXCIV ACGKR FIVGK PWGCG BXVEC XGGWR AUWPE VQRFP
    CFKRT CGWPP VYFKC AQVXK DCXWK DCXUW PEUYG KCXKX CFAVQ
    KDCUR GK

CHAPTER THREE

Polyalphabetic Substitution

3.1 Polyalphabetic ciphers

The preceding chapter has indicated how a monoalphabetic cipher can be solved. Even if the original word lengths are concealed and the substitution alphabet is random, it is possible to find a solution by using frequency data, repetition patterns and information about the way letters combine with one another. What makes the solution possible is the fact that a given plain language letter is always represented by the same cipher letter. As a consequence, all the properties of plain language such as frequencies and combinations are carried over into the cipher and may be utilized for solution. In effect we could say that all such properties are invariant except that the names of the letters have been changed.

It would seem then that one way to obtain greater security would be to use more than one alphabet in enciphering a message. The general system could be one that uses a number of different alphabets for encipherment, with an understanding between the correspondents of the order in which the alphabets are to be used.

As an illustration of a classic procedure, consider the method that was devised by the French cryptographer Vigenère. It utilizes the encipherment square which is known by his name—the Vigenère square—described in Chapter 1 (pp. 11–12). This square, whose successive rows consist of the normal alphabet shifted by 1 place, 2 places, etc., can be easily constructed whenever it is needed. In addition, the correspondents agree on a keyword, and this is the only thing that needs to be memorized. The general system consists in the successive use of the alphabets designated by the letters of the keyword to encipher successive letters of the plain text.

For example, suppose the keyword is SYMBOL, and the message to be enciphered is

```
THE ATOMIC ENERGY COMMISSION SAID YESTERDAY THAT RADIATION
FROM AN UNDERGROUND NUCLEAR BLAST LEAKED INTO THE
ATMOSPHERE TWO OR THREE HOURS AFTER A LOW YIELD NUCLEAR
BOMB WAS TRIGGERED IN THE YUCCA BASIN
```

The encipherment would proceed as follows: the first letter, T_p, of the message would be enciphered by means of alphabet S (the first letter of the keyword SYMBOL). The cipher sequence of the substitution alphabet is the row of the Vigenère square beginning with the letter S. The cipher equivalent for T_p would be found in the square at the intersection of column T and row S. It is L_c. The second letter, H_p, would be enciphered by means of alphabet Y. The resulting cipher F_c is the intersection of column H and row Y. The process continues with successive letters of the keyword selecting the enciphering alphabet for successive letters of the message until the keyword is used up, in our example with the encipherment of the sixth letter of the message.

```
Key letter    S Y M B O L
    Plain     t h e a t o
   Cipher     L F Q B H Z
```

Starting with the seventh letter, the same set of alphabets is used in succession to encipher the next six letters, then the next six, etc. until the entire message has been enciphered.

The encipherer (or decipherer) does not need to reproduce the entire square to carry out the necessary operations. It is sufficient to generate just those lines of the square that correspond to the letters of the keyword:

```
A B C D E F G H I J K L M N O P Q R S T U V W X Y Z
─────────────────────────────────────────────────
S T U V W X Y Z A B C D E F G H I J K L M N O P Q R
Y Z A B C D E F G H I J K L M N O P Q R S T U V W X
M N O P Q R S T U V W X Y Z A B C D E F G H I J K L
B C D E F G H I J K L M N O P Q R S T U V W X Y Z A
O P Q R S T U V W X Y Z A B C D E F G H I J K L M N
L M N O P Q R S T U V W X Y Z A B C D E F G H I J K
```

Note that the mechanics of encipherment can be simplified by writing out the message in six columns. Then all the letters in one column would be enciphered by the same alphabet. Thus, having selected alphabet S, the encipherer can apply it to all the letters of column 1.

```
S Y M B O L
t h e a t o
L
m i c e n e
E
r g y c o m
J
m i s s i o
E
. . . . . .
. . . . . .
```

With alphabet Y he can encipher all the letters of column 2, etc. This eliminates the need to jump from alphabet to alphabet as the encipherment progresses from letter to letter.

In the language of modular arithmetic every letter whose position number in the original message is congruent to a modulo 6 would be enciphered by the alphabet designated by the a-th letter of the keyword. This kind of general system which selects a set of alphabets and uses them repeatedly in the same order is called a *polyalphabetic cipher system*.

If we go through the complete process of enciphering the message on page 59 with the keyword SYMBOL, the results are:

```
Key     S Y M B O L  S Y M B O L  S Y M B O L  S Y M B O L  S Y M B O L

Plain   t h e a t o  m i c e n e  r g y c o m  m i s s i o  n s a i d y
Cipher  L F Q B H Z  E G O F B P  J E K D C X  E G E T W Z  F Q M J R J

Plain   e s t e r d  a y t h a t  r a d i a t  i o n f r o  m a n u n d
Cipher  W Q F F F O  S W F I O E  J Y P J O E  A M Z G F Z  E Y Z V B O

Plain   e r g r o u  n d n u c l  e a r b l a  s t l e a k  e d i n t o
Cipher  W P S S C F  F B Z V Q W  W Y D C Z L  K R X F O V  W B U O H Z

Plain   t h e a t m  o s p h e r  e t w o o r  t h r e e h  o u r s a f
Cipher  L F Q B H X  G Q B I S C  W R I P C C  L F D F S S  G S D T O Q

Plain   t e r a l o  w y i e l d  n u c l e a  r b o m b w  a s t r i g
Cipher  L C D B Z Z  O W U F Z O  F S O M S L  J Z A N P H  S Q F S W R

Plain   g e r e d i  n t h e y u  c c a b a s  i n
Cipher  Y C D F R T  F R T F M F  U A M C O D  A L
```

The cipher message is then rewritten in five letter groups for transmission.

In this cipher message, any particular cipher letter may represent
one of six different plain text letters, depending on its position in the
message. Note, for example, that the word *nuclear* appears twice in
the plain language message. It is enciphered the first time by the
letters ZVQWWYD and the second time by FSOMSLJ. There is
no relationship between these two encipherments. We even note that
each encipherment contains a repeated letter where none appears in
the original word. No longer is it possible to associate the frequency
of each cipher letter with that of a particular plain text letter. Repeated plain text letters may be replaced by different cipher letters,
and a repeated cipher letter may represent different plain letters.

If there is a regular exchange of messages between the correspondents, it can be additionally agreed, for further security, to
change the keyword from time to time, perhaps even with each new
message.

Exercise

41. Decipher the following message which was enciphered by means of a
Vigenère square and the keyword HOUSE:

```
AVYUL HWLEE UCZLL LTYVI YOFJI ZSLNI ICUJH ZOCVC LGNWV
KOSLL HHULE EWHUV LOMWM ZBYWH LRHGA
```

3.2 Recognition of polyalphabetic ciphers

The methods of Chapter 2 for solving a monoalphabet are no
longer applicable to the solution of a cipher of this character. How
then could a cryptanalyst deal with such a problem? The techniques
used will be illustrated by applying them to an example. Suppose
that the cipher message we wish to solve is:

```
APWVC DKPAK BCECY WXBBK CYVSE FVTLV MXGRG KKGFD LRLZK
TFVKH SAGUK YEXSR SIQTW JXVFL LALUI KYABZ XGRKL BAFSJ
CCMJT ZDGST AHBJM MLGEZ RPZIJ XPVGU OJXHL PUMVM CKYEX
SRSIQ KCWMC KFLQJ FWJRH SWLOX YPVKM HYCTA WEJVQ DPAVV
KFLKG FDLRL ZKIWT IBXSG RTPLL AMHFR OMEMV ZQZGK MSDFH
ATXSE ELVWK OCJFQ FLHRJ SMVMV IMBOZ HIKRO MUHIE RYG
```

A monographic distribution for this message yields:

```
A B C D E F G H I J K L M N O P Q R S T U V W X Y Z
≠ ≠ ≠ ≠ ≠ ≠ ≠ ≠ ≠ ≠ ≠ ≠   ≠ ≠ ≠ ≠ ≠ ≠ ≠ ≠ ≠ ≠ ≠
≠ = ≠ − ≠ ≠ ≠ ≠ = ≠ ≠ ≠   − = − ≠ ≠ ≡   ≠ ≡ ≠ = ≡
− −     ≡ =       − ≠ ≠ ≠           ≡ ≡     ≠   −
              ≠ = −                               −
```

This distribution shows a good deal of variation in the frequencies of the individual letters—from K which occurs 20 times to N which does not occur at all. And yet, it isn't like the distribution of a monoalphabetic cipher. It has a much flatter appearance. Note, in particular, how few low frequency letters there are.

If we think about our illustrative polyalphabetic example, we can understand why we might expect a flatter looking distribution. Since our example used the *six*-letter keyword SYMBOL, any given cipher letter may have *six* different plain letter equivalents. Which of these six is the correct correspondent depends on the position of the given cipher letter in the message. For example, if A_c occurs in the first, or seventh, or thirteenth—i.e. in the 1st (modulo 6)—position, its plain letter equivalent is I_p, because in those positions the S alphabet was used for encipherment, and in that alphabet A_c corresponds to I_p:

```
Cipher:   S  T  U  V  W  X  Y  Z |A| B  .  .  .
Plain:    A  B  C  D  E  F  G  H |I| J  .  .  .
```

Similarly, if A_c occurs in the second position (modulo 6), its plain letter equivalent is C_p because the Y alphabet, as cipher, yields the correspondence $A_c \rightarrow C_p$:

```
Cipher:   Y  Z |A| B  .  .  .
Plain:    A  B |C| D  .  .  .
```

A_c occurring in third, fourth, fifth, sixth positions (modulo 6) yields O_p, Z_p, M_p and P_p, respectively. If we transcribe the original message in six columns, then the j-th column represents ciphers in the j-th position (modulo six) of the message, and each column has a different deciphering alphabet.

We would expect a given plain text letter to appear as frequently in one column as in another. In other words, the relative frequency of a given plain text letter is expected to be the same in each column as it is in the whole message. For a long message, the relative frequency of any letter in a given column should approximate the characteristic frequency of that letter. Hence the number of occurrences of A_c in column 1 would be determined by the characteristic frequency of I_p. The number of occurrences of A_c in column 2 would be determined by the characteristic frequency of C_p, etc. The number of occurrences of A_c in the entire message would be approximately equal to the average of the characteristic frequencies of the set of plain letters I, C, O, Z, M, P.

Similarly any other cipher letter will have a frequency approximating the average of the characteristic frequency of a set of six plain language letters. There is consequently a tendency for the relative frequencies of the cipher letters *to average out.* In effect this means that the crests and troughs of the frequency distribution of the cipher message will be less pronounced than in the standard plain language distribution. Of course, the greater the number of different alphabets used, the more nearly will the cipher distribution take on a completely flattened appearance. And if all 26 alphabets are used we would expect the relative frequencies of all the cipher letters to be approximately equal.

We should therefore be able to recognize from the frequency distribution of a polyalphabetic cipher message that it has not resulted from the use of one single alphabet. Often this is evident just by inspection of the frequency distribution. But if the message is short, or if a small number of alphabets has been used, a look at the frequency distribution may not be conclusive at all.

The property that distinguishes the monoalphabetic distribution from that corresponding to a polyalphabetic message is that the monoalphabet has a greater variation among the frequencies of the individual letters.

By the amount of variation or "roughness" of a distribution we mean, qualitatively speaking, the amount by which individual frequencies differ. For example, if all letters occurred with the same frequency, the distribution would look flat, and there would be zero variation. In order to use this concept of variation as a tool in our work, we must give a precise quantitative definition of it which will enable us to measure this property of a distribution accurately.

In the theory of probability, the relative frequency of an event x is defined as

$$\frac{\text{the number of occurrences of } x}{\text{the total number of experiments}}.$$

Here, each experiment consists in examining a letter in some text, and the occurrence of a particular letter, say B, might be the event in question. If B occurs 48 times in a text of 1000 letters, the relative frequency of B would be

$$\frac{f_B}{1000} = \frac{48}{1000} = .048,$$

where f_B denotes the number of occurrences of B.

Clearly, if we add all the relative frequencies of the 26 letters in our sample text of 1000 letters, we would get

$$\frac{f_A}{1000} + \frac{f_B}{1000} + \cdots + \frac{f_Z}{1000} = \frac{1000}{1000} = 1.$$

The probability of occurrence of an event x is defined as the limit of relative frequencies of x as the total number n of experiments increases. For example, the probability p_B of occurrence of B is

$$p_B = \lim_{n \to \infty} \frac{\text{the number of occurrences of B}}{n}.$$

If all letters of the alphabet occurred with the same frequency, we would have

$$f_A = f_B = \cdots = f_Z$$

and hence all relative frequencies would be equal. Since

$$\sum_{i=A}^{i=Z} \frac{f_i}{n} = 1,$$

we can conclude that

$$\frac{f_A}{n} = \frac{f_B}{n} = \cdots = \frac{f_Z}{n} = \frac{1}{26},$$

and hence that the probabilities are all equal:

$$p_A = p_B = \cdots = p_Z = \frac{1}{26}.$$

We know that the 26 letters of the alphabet do not occur with equal frequencies and that therefore their probabilities $p_A, p_B, \cdots$ are not all equal. They have positive values between zero and one and add up to 1 (see page 17):

$$\sum_{i=A}^{i=Z} p_i = 1.$$

The amount by which p_A differs from 1/26, i.e. its deviation from the average probability, is $p_A - (1/26)$. Similarly the amount by which the probability of occurrence of B differs from the average is $p_B - (1/26)$, etc. A measure of roughness of the distribution would be a function of these 26 quantities $p_i - (1/26)$, where i is a variable which takes the values A, B, C, $\cdots$, Z.

This desired measure could not be anything as simple as just the sum of the deviations because some are positive and some are negative. They balance out when added and give an answer zero. For,

$$\sum_{i=A}^{i=Z} \left(p_i - \frac{1}{26} \right) = \sum_{i=A}^{i=Z} p_i - \sum_{i=A}^{i=Z} \frac{1}{26} = 1 - 26\frac{1}{26} = 0.$$

To get around the problem of having both positive and negative numbers, we could take the sum of the magnitudes or the absolute values of the deviations

$$\sum_{i=A}^{i=Z} \left| p_i - \frac{1}{26} \right|.$$

But this measure has disadvantages stemming in part from the awkwardness of working with the absolute value function.

Another way to make all the terms positive is to square each deviation. The sum of the squares of the deviations is a quantity commonly utilized in statistical work. For that reason we shall choose as the *measure of roughness*, which we shall call M.R., the quantity defined by

$$\text{M.R.} = \left(p_A - \frac{1}{26}\right)^2 + \left(p_B - \frac{1}{26}\right)^2 + \cdots + \left(p_Z - \frac{1}{26}\right)^2$$

or in shorthand notation

$$\text{M.R.} = \sum_{i=A}^{i=Z} \left(p_i - \frac{1}{26}\right)^2.$$

The calculation of M.R. can be made easier by an algebraic simplification of the above expression. If we square the binomial $p_i - (1/26)$ we have

$$p_i^2 - 2p_i\left(\frac{1}{26}\right) + \left(\frac{1}{26}\right)^2.$$

Summing this expression for all the values of i from A to Z, we obtain

$$\text{M.R.} = \sum_{i=A}^{i=Z} p_i^2 - \sum_{i=A}^{i=Z} 2p_i\left(\frac{1}{26}\right) + \sum_{i=A}^{i=Z} \left(\frac{1}{26}\right)^2.$$

Since $(1/26)^2$ is the same whatever value i takes on, the last term is $26(1/26)^2$ or $1/26$. The middle term is

$$2\left(\frac{1}{26}\right) \sum_{i=A}^{i=Z} p_i;$$

since $\sum_{i=A}^{i=Z} p_i = 1$, the middle term reduces to $2(1/26)$. Therefore

$$\text{M.R.} = \sum_{i=A}^{i=Z} p_i^2 - 2\left(\frac{1}{26}\right) + \frac{1}{26} = \sum_{i=A}^{i=Z} p_i^2 - \frac{1}{26},$$

$$\text{M.R.} \approx \sum_{i=A}^{i=Z} p_i^2 - .038.$$

If we were dealing with a plain language distribution, we could calculate M.R. by summing the squares of all the characteristic frequencies and subtracting .038. We know the characteristic frequencies of the letters of plain text (page 16). If we sum their squares we get .066. Thus M.R. for plain text is .066 − .038 = .028. For a distribution which is flat, i.e. one in which all letters have the same probability of occurrence, $p_i = 1/26$ for all values of i. In this case

$$\sum_{i=A}^{i=Z} p_i^2 = \sum_{i=A}^{i=Z} \left(\frac{1}{26}\right)^2 = 26 \left(\frac{1}{26}\right)^2 = \frac{1}{26}, \quad \text{and} \quad \text{M.R.} = \frac{1}{26} - \frac{1}{26} = 0.$$

Thus the measure of roughness varies from 0 when the distribution is flat to a value of .028 for a monoalphabet. This variation proves sufficient to permit us to distinguish between monoalphabets and polyalphabets, provided we are able to determine $\sum_{i=A}^{i=Z} p_i^2$.

But if we are given a distribution for a cipher message like the one we wish to solve, we have no knowledge of the probabilities of the equivalent plain letters. We could calculate them for a message like our illustrative example in which we know all the substitution alphabets and hence all the plain language equivalents any cipher letter may have. In an unknown situation no such information is available to us.

What we need to do is to find some other way of approximating $\sum_{i=A}^{i=Z} p_i^2$. Let us consider one term of this sum, say p_A^2. Can we assign some significance to this number? First, what does p_A mean? It is the probability that an arbitrarily selected letter in the cipher will be an A. Then p_A^2 represents the probability that two letters selected at random will both be A.[†] Similarly p_B^2 represents the probability that two letters selected at random will both be B, and so on for each letter. The probability that two letters picked at random would be the same regardless of their identity is

$$p_A^2 + p_B^2 + \cdots + p_Z^2 = \sum_{i=A}^{i=Z} p_i^2 .[‡]$$

[†] See e.g. J. P. Hoyt, *Probability Theory*, International Textbook Co., Scranton, Penna., 1967, p. 29.
[‡] Ibid., p. 27.

Here now is a means of approximating $\sum_A^Z p_i^2$† without a knowledge of the quantities p_i. It is the probability that two letters chosen at random will be the same. What we need to do is to count how many pairs of identical letters there are in the cipher message and divide that number by the total number of possible pairs.

To do this we need to answer the question: How many pairs of letters can be formed from a given set? Suppose we have x letters in the set. Then the number of pairs we can get is determined as follows. As a first choice we can select any one of the letters. That makes x possibilities. There then remain $x - 1$ letters for the second choice making a total of $x(x - 1)$ possibilities. But, in this count, each pair has been counted twice since the same pair can be obtained in two different orders. Therefore, the number of pairs of letters that can be chosen from a set of x is $\frac{1}{2}x(x - 1)$.

If the observed frequency of A in the cipher message is f_A, then the number of pairs of A's that can be formed from these f_A letters is $\frac{1}{2}f_A(f_A - 1)$. The number of pairs of B's is $\frac{1}{2}f_B(f_B - 1)$. The total number of like pairs regardless of the identity of the letter is the sum

$$\sum_{i=A}^{i=Z} \frac{f_i(f_i - 1)}{2}.$$

If the total number of letters is N, then the total possible number of pairs of letters is $\frac{1}{2}N(N - 1)$. Since the chance of two letters being alike is the number of like pairs divided by the total number of pairs, we get

$$\frac{\sum_{i=A}^{i=Z} f_i(f_i - 1)}{N(N - 1)}.$$

This number is a good estimate for $\sum_A^Z p_i^2$. Since it represents the chance that two letters in a distribution are alike, it is called the *index of coincidence* and is abbreviated I.C.

It is more usual in cryptanalysis to work with the quantity I.C. than with M.R. We have seen that M.R. $= \sum_A^Z p_i^2 - .038$ and that it varies from 0 to .028. Therefore $\sum_A^Z p_i^2 = $ M.R. $+ .038$ varies from .038 to .066. Since the quantity I.C. approximates $\sum_A^Z p_i^2$, it

† The symbol $\sum_A^Z$ abbreviates the symbol $\sum_{i=A}^{i=Z}$.

has the same range of variation: .038 to .066. The lower bound corresponds to a flat distribution, and the upper bound corresponds to monoalphabeticity.

A measure of how this variation of values is related to the number of alphabets and hence to the flatness of the distribution can be calculated by statistical methods which are beyond the scope of this text. If a message of N letters is enciphered by m alphabets, each alphabet being applied to the same total number of plain text letters, the expected value that would be obtained for I.C. can be shown to be

$$\text{I.C.} = \frac{1}{m} \frac{N-m}{N-1} (.066) + \frac{m-1}{m} \frac{N}{N-1} (.038).$$

If N is a relatively large number, the I.C. for specific values of m (the number of alphabets) can be readily approximated by means of this expression; a few values are listed below:

m	I.C.
1	.066
2	.052
5	.044
10	.041
large	.038

It must be emphasized that these results for the index of coincidence are statistical in nature. They apply to situations where N is a large number, i.e. for very long messages. For short messages the calculated values of I.C. may differ considerably from these expected values. One should not therefore base any firm conclusions concerning the number of alphabets used to encipher a short message merely on the I.C. of that message. To illustrate: if we calculate I.C. for the example at the beginning of the chapter, we get .049 which is about what we would expect if there were three alphabets. Yet we know that six alphabets were used.

Another point to be kept in mind is that the expected value of the I.C. was based on the assumption that each alphabet was applied to the same number of letters. This would not be true if there were repeated letters in the keyword of a polyalphabetic message. So, the information furnished by I.C. about the number of alphabets in a cipher message must be treated as an approximate result.

However it can certainly give a good indication of whether a message is monoalphabetic. If we calculate I.C. for our unknown message on page 61, we get .041. This number, we have seen, is the value that might theoretically be expected if there are as many as ten alphabets. We can therefore feel reasonably certain that our unknown message is not monoalphabetic, and we would not devote any effort toward trying to solve it by the methods of Chapter 2.

Exercises

42. Apply the I.C. test to the monographic distributions on (a) page 28 and (b) page 34 and confirm that the results suggest that the messages are monoalphabetic.

43. Given the monographic distributions of five cipher messages, calculate the I.C.'s and determine which messages are monoalphabetic. Then arrange the others in the probable order of increasing number of cipher alphabets.

1.
A	B	C	D	E	F	G	H	I	J	K	L	M	N	O	P	Q	R	S	T	U	V	W	X	Y	Z
7	6	9	3	5	6	8	3	4	7	13	10	7	0	1	5	3	6	8	5	4	8	4	8	5	5

2.
A	B	C	D	E	F	G	H	I	J	K	L	M	N	O	P	Q	R	S	T	U	V	W	X	Y	Z
5	3	10	0	1	4	9	0	0	9	3	10	5	2	0	6	5	10	4	2	0	0	1	0	8	0

3.
A	B	C	D	E	F	G	H	I	J	K	L	M	N	O	P	Q	R	S	T	U	V	W	X	Y	Z
4	6	6	11	13	6	3	6	8	8	9	7	1	2	6	9	8	12	8	4	2	11	7	1	11	7

4.
A	B	C	D	E	F	G	H	I	J	K	L	M	N	O	P	Q	R	S	T	U	V	W	X	Y	Z
3	0	3	6	17	1	0	1	5	1	8	6	2	7	0	4	1	5	0	1	4	1	13	1	0	9

5.
A	B	C	D	E	F	G	H	I	J	K	L	M	N	O	P	Q	R	S	T	U	V	W	X	Y	Z
3	7	4	2	8	5	6	4	10	5	8	6	8	3	7	9	5	6	4	9	5	7	3	7	6	3

3.3 Determination of number of alphabets

Once we know that the message we are trying to solve involves more than one alphabet, our next problem is to determine how many alphabets were employed and whether they have been used in the repetitive fashion of a polyalphabet.† In a polyalphabetic message, *written out* in a number of columns equal to the number of letters of the keyword, all the letters in the same column are enciphered

---

† The technique for recognizing polyalphabetic ciphers was first published by a Prussian military officer, Friedrich W. Kasiski, in 1863.

by the same monoalphabet. If therefore a word (or any sequence of letters) is repeated in the plain language message and happens to fall in the same columns each time, it will produce identical encipherments. Note, for example, in the illustrative message on page 59 how the initial word *the* and the first two letters of *atomic* fall in the same columns as the word *the* and the letters *at* of *atmosphere*. In both cases, the cipher for *theat* is LFQBH. The interval between such identical encipherments (i.e., the number of letters between them) is equal to a multiple of the length "k" of the keyword. To see this, note that corresponding letters of such repetitions are in positions congruent to the same number modulo k. Therefore the difference of their position numbers is congruent to zero modulo k.

It is true that different plain text letters in different columns may be replaced by the same cipher letters. It is also true that different plain text digraphs and trigraphs may be enciphered identically. For example, in the last line of the message on page 60, the cipher sequence FRT, which occurs twice in succession, arises from plain letters *edi* in one case and *nth* in another. The probability that a cipher repetition is of this "accidental" kind becomes less and less as the number of letters in the repetition increases. Clearly the longer the repetition that is found, the more likely is it to represent a causal situation—an actual plain text repetition.

One means then of deciding if a message is polyalphabetic is to determine what cipher repetitions exist in it and to see whether the intervals between these repetitions have any common factor. Such a common factor would be a candidate for the number of letters in the keyword. We shall illustrate this procedure using the message on page 61.

In order to find repetitions we make a trigraphic frequency distribution of the message, in the manner described in Chapter 2. The distribution is given in Figure 6. With its aid, the cryptanalyst will be assured of finding all the repetitions the message contains.

We find two quite long repetitions (see page 73), and we note the position in the message of the first letter of each occurrence. The interval between the repetitions is the difference between the position numbers of the corresponding letters. (There are also several trigraphic repetitions in the message, but we need not consider them since the evidence from the long repetitions is much more significant.)

A	B	C	D	E	F	G	H	I	J	K	L	M	N	O	P	Q	R	S	T	U	V	W	X	Y	Z
.P	KC	VD	CK	CC	EV	XR	KS	SQ	WX	DP	TV	VX	UJ		AW	IT	GG	VE	VL	GK	WC	PV	WB	CW	LK
PK	XB	BE	FL	GD	SF	RK	AB	SC	UK	AB	DR	CJ	LX		KA	IK	LL	HA	KF	LI	YS	YX	MG	CV	BX
SG	BK	EY	ZG	YX	TV	KF	XL	ZJ	MT	BC	RZ	JM	RM		RZ	LJ	SS	XR	QW	GO	FT	TJ	ES	KE	TD
LL	AZ	KY	QP	GZ	VL	AU	RS	SQ	BM	GK	FL	ML	KC		XV	VD	GK	RI	JZ	PM	LM	CM	JV	KA	ER
YB	LA	JC	FL	YX	AS	XR	MY	KW	IX	KG	LA	UV	BZ		LU	ZZ	ZP	FJ	SA	MH	FK	FJ	ZG	KE	PI
BF	HJ	CM	SF	WJ	KL	DS	MF	TB	OX	VH	AU	VC	RM		YV	FF	SS	GT	CA		XF	SL	JP	XP	LK
TH	IX	MK	MK	MM	YX	LE	FA	VM	QF	UY	MG	KB		DA			JH	XR	WI		PG	AW		HC	VQ
TW	MO	KW	SE	KL	VU	LR	HK	WR	UY	IY	HP	KH		TL			LL	RI	RP		MM	IT	ES	RG	QG
PV		MK			IR	SR		UI									GT	HW	AX	PK	PK	VK	OY		OH
LM		YT			DH	ZK											FO	XG		JQ	AV		BS		
HT	OJ				JQ			Y.									HJ	MD		VK	MZ		TS		

Figure 6

Repeated Sequence	Positions of first letter	Interval
KGFDLRLZK	37, 184	147
KYEXSRSIQ	55, 132	77

Since these repetitions are much too long to be accidental, and since the only common factor of both intervals is 7, the evidence is very strongly in favor of the message being polyalphabetic, with seven alphabets. The index of coincidence which we had calculated (see p. 69) is consistent with this conclusion.

If it is correct that there are seven alphabets, then all the cipher letters whose positions are congruent to one another modulo 7 should be in one alphabet. To confirm this, we write out the message in 7 columns.†

```
APWVCDK PAKBCEC YWXBBKC YVSEFVT LVMXGRG KKGFDLR LZKTFVK
HSAGUKY EXSRSIQ TWJXVFL LALUIKY ABZXGRK LBAFSJC CMJTZDG
STAHBJM MLGEZRP ZIJXPVG UOJXHLP UMVMCKY EXSRSIQ KCWMCKF
LQJFWJR HSWLOXY PVKMHYC TAWEJVQ DPAVVKF LKGFDLR LZKIWTI
BXSGRTP LLAMHFR OMEMVZQ ZGKMSDF HATXSEE LVWKOCJ FQFLHRJ
SMVMVIM BOZHIKR OMUHIER YG
```

We now prepare a monographic distribution for each column, with the results shown on the next page.

These look like good monoalphabets. But we need not be content with general impressions. We have a means now, through the use of indices of coincidence, to derive a numerical measure of mono-alphabeticity. If we calculate I.C. for these seven distributions, we get

1	2	3	4	5	6	7
.070	.050	.071	.072	.051	.071	.066

Except for distributions 2 and 5, the results are indicative of good monoalphabetic distributions. Even 2 and 5 give results better than the index for the entire message for which we found an I.C. of .041.

† Each of the seven columns would be so long that, for typographical reasons, we just grouped the letters by sevens; this shows at a glance which letter is in which column.

A B C D E F G H I J K L M N O P Q R S T U V W X Y Z   Column 1

A B C D E F G H I J K L M N O P Q R S T U V W X Y Z   Column 2

A B C D E F G H I J K L M N O P Q R S T U V W X Y Z   Column 3

A B C D E F G H I J K L M N O P Q R S T U V W X Y Z   Column 4

A B C D E F G H I J K L M N O P Q R S T U V W X Y Z   Column 5

A B C D E F G H I J K L M N O P Q R S T U V W X Y Z   Column 6

A B C D E F G H I J K L M N O P Q R S T U V W X Y Z   Column 7

An overall index for the message on the basis of its division into seven alphabets could be formed by getting the average of these I.C.'s. This turns out to be .064, almost the same as the I.C. for plain language. We are justified in continuing with the assumption that the cipher is a polyalphabet with seven alphabets.

Exercises

Determine the number of alphabets used in the encipherment of the messages given below.

```
44. SBPRT LHMWW OAHHE SCNQO RWDPM UVZKG NDMAZ AGENB BBASH
    YQEKU HWTBR XJOTI IAJHV PIWZK FOHCQ PNHFP QQBAK ZJXWH
    RVCYG GOKES LNCEK VFPHW GKDMT OMAGT ZPNUN TLCMZ KBSWO
    YDVGK YFLGX NXLCQ OPRUU SLIMA BAFZI URTLO YYBBL GFXPT
    NZWBP RIAJE CCZIQ BSBNZ LUEHC ECMFK KBPZL RJLCC ZDRGD
    GNDMA ZATTX ARIJS ENTBT YVTYL RTABE CMBIW OYYMR VK
```

45. CNPWV BAGYW OFGWC YYBQZ DELTY AABAD AAGHL DLPHD DNZYC
    KFPPU UPPJC HUPFC FPBQX AACUF MPPNL OYPAL DNVAZ DDMWZ
    JPMXF JYDKC YPVNF JLYKL TPLGY FDPAL FRIKK XUMYY JPMTB
    CNPWV BAGYW OFGWC YIGNV MRDGD KFPKO ZARKK KAJGD DNBQF
    QBVRL IQNQD MQGDF YPHHL DQGHQ MATGI JPMAT JEUKB UUDRK
    KIVAC QACKN KIGIE FQKRK ZU

3.4 Solution of individual alphabets, if standard

Let us examine the monoalphabetic distributions more critically now. Could they perhaps represent direct standard alphabets? If the system of encipherment uses a Vigenère square, as described at the beginning of this chapter, then they represent standard alphabets, and we should be able to match the standard distribution against these columnar distributions. When we try to do this, it proves difficult to be sure of the correct match in all cases. The number of letters represented in the distributions is not large and the characteristic frequencies do not show through very clearly.

However, alphabet 3 with $S_c = A_p$ looks like an excellent match. Alphabet 4 with $T_c = A_p$ and alphabet 6 with $R_c = A_p$ look good. If these values are correct, we can decipher all the letters in the corresponding columns and see what probable text results. Here are the decipherments of the first twelve letters in columns 3, 4, and 6:

E	C	.	M
S	I	.	N
F	I	.	T
A	L	.	E
U	E	.	A
O	M	.	U
S	A	.	E
I	N	.	T
A	Y	.	R
R	E	.	O
T	B	.	T
H	E	.	A

The combinations look good. We see a number of high frequency digraphs in columns 3 and 4 and nothing that looks impossible. The evidence for direct standard alphabets seems very strong.

To extend these results, the obvious next step would be to try to solve column 5. If it is a direct standard alphabet, as seems very likely, then all its possible decipherments would be obtained by completing the plain component, as described on page 15.

We write down the first twelve letters of column 5 and complete the plain component. Then we examine each of the rows in turn seeking a good selection of plain text letters to be inserted for the missing letters in the already deciphered combinations. The row beginning with O is found to be the correct choice.

												Sums of frequencies	Sums of log weights
C	C	B	F	G	D	F	U	S	V	I	G	38	17.067
D	D	C	G	H	E	G	V	T	W	J	H	48	16.963
E	E	D	H	I	F	H	W	U	X	K	I	60	17.956
F	F	E	I	J	G	I	X	V	Y	L	J	42	15.188
G	G	F	J	K	H	J	Y	W	Z	M	K	18	10.836
H	H	G	K	L	I	K	Z	X	A	N	L	40	14.657
I	I	H	L	M	J	L	A	Y	B	O	M	49	17.432
J	J	I	M	N	K	M	B	Z	C	P	N	36	13.390
K	K	J	N	O	L	N	C	A	D	Q	O	48	15.782
L	L	K	O	P	M	O	D	B	E	R	P	56	18.162
M	M	L	P	Q	N	P	E	C	F	S	Q	49	16.885
N	N	M	Q	R	O	Q	F	D	G	T	R	60	18.043
O	O	N	R	S	P	R	G	E	H	U	S	74	20.726
P	P	O	S	T	Q	S	H	F	I	V	T	58	18.718
Q	Q	P	T	U	R	T	I	G	J	W	U	47	15.650
R	R	Q	U	V	S	U	J	H	K	X	V	34	15.161
S	S	R	V	W	T	V	K	I	L	Y	W	48	17.259
T	T	S	W	X	U	W	L	J	M	Z	X	38	13.217
U	U	T	X	Y	V	X	M	K	N	A	Y	38	15.531
V	V	U	Y	Z	W	Y	N	L	O	B	Z	31	13.680
W	W	V	Z	A	X	Z	O	M	P	C	A	35	14.122
X	X	W	A	B	Y	A	P	N	Q	D	B	35	14.959
Y	Y	X	B	C	Z	B	Q	O	R	E	C	40	14.466
Z	Z	Y	C	D	A	C	R	P	S	F	D	43	15.918
A	A	Z	D	E	B	D	S	Q	T	G	E	66	17.645
B	B	A	E	F	C	E	T	R	U	H	F	67	19.201

Actually, the correct row can be selected from the above array by frequency considerations alone and without examining how the letters fit into the portions of text on page 75. What is desired is the row that has the most likely collection of plain text letters. It can be found by recording the characteristic frequency of each letter, adding these frequencies for each row, and noting which row produces the highest sum. The sums are shown to the right of the individual rows and we note that the highest result is for the row beginning with the letter O. Actually, from the point of view of probability theory, the correct way to assign a weight to each row is to determine the product of all the characteristic frequencies appearing in that row. This would require a more tedious calculation which can be simplified by replacing the frequencies by their logarithms and then adding these *log weights*. A table of log weights derived from 2-place logs is provided in Appendix B. If we sum the log weights for each row, we again find that the O row is the best choice.

When we add the letters from the O row to the text of columns 3, 4, and 6 we have results from just the first 12 letters which convince us that we are on the right track.

E	C	O	M
S	I	O	N
F	I	N	T
A	L	R	E
U	E	S	A
O	M	P	U
S	A	R	E
I	N	G	T
A	Y	E	R
R	E	H	O
T	B	U	T
H	E	S	A

The next step would be to complete the plain component for column 2 to find the correct letters preceding the above tetragraphs or, alternatively, to work with column 7 to find the correct letters following the above tetragraphs. Continuing in this way, the original plain text is determined and the message is found to read:

```
THE COMMISSIONER OF INTERNAL REVENUE SAID
COMPUTERS ARE MAKING TAXPAYERS MORE HONEST BUT
AT THE SAME TIME SEVERAL MILLIONS OF DOLLARS ARE
```

BEING RETURNED TO TAXPAYERS DUE TO THEIR MISTAKES
AGAINST THEMSELVES WHICH THE COMPUTERS PICK UP
AND CREDIT TO THEM THIS SYSTEM HAS BEEN GENERALLY
INSTALLED THROUGHOUT THE COUNTRY

The equivalents of A_p in the seven alphabets are

$$
\begin{array}{cc}
1 & H \\
2 & I \\
3 & S \\
4 & T \\
5 & O \\
6 & R \\
7 & Y \\
\end{array}
$$

and give the keyword for the encipherment of the message.

Exercises

Solve:

46. The message given in Exercise 44.

47. POMMG EAMVL PHBWL YVUET JKVWT NZIAZ KUIFG KBVUX ZFMKM
    AYLSR POILM DPZLX AUBZH QZIFW WTMJB YHVKH QAPNB AAVSF
    AZMSN OAZSE EHVSG ZUMOS AHTSG ZMWJV AZPSO ASIMG YOMVT
    JLEGY BLVKB RLIYT EUALM DLDAX PJWFZ BPNLR IPTWL AHALH
    BZIAZ KU

3.5 Polyalphabetic ciphers with a mixed plain sequence

As the informed cryptographer might have expected, the use of
direct standard alphabets in Vigenère's system carries with it the
disadvantage of linearity. The identification of one letter in a direct
standard alphabet determines the complete alphabet.

The security could be much improved if the alphabets were unsystematic. It will be recalled (see page 40) that an alphabet can be
made random by mixing either the plain or the cipher sequence. It
would follow then that all 26 alphabets of the Vigenère square
can be made unsystematic simply by changing the plain sequence to
a mixed sequence. If that is done, it will no longer be possible to fit
a standard distribution to the individual distributions resulting from
the cipher message.

That will be our next type of problem for study. The cipher message we wish to solve is

```
SWWJR GPRDN FMWJE XEWGR ZJQDN VJZRV SZXOJ VWWRO VBHRM
MOFDL IPAXV EZWUT CZOZA AQQJL UPKZZ XUMJA PCZOE BAWZR
ZYKZI POFOL UOCRE NYKRI CAMOX IOORR ZJKOL VWWJN VPKZA
AFOCA MZOMR CJZDY EJXEL XRFQI ZJCMA RJVWI DSWZX ASOTR
BJBZO QPXMI PDJVZ ZXHGQ SZFDQ FJZJR BMWIC EZMWL MECVY
VWZOX TWHSR UUBMT NSJDW SSOOW CUNJY VJEWI PPFSL MOQVY
CVWRI SMMHW XMEJY NUZMV MXWCR NBRDE SNB
```

The index of coincidence is .046. It is practically certain that the message is not a monoalphabet.

A trigraphic frequency study—we shall not reproduce it here—finds no repetitions longer than a trigraph. There are nine trigraphic repetitions with intervals as indicated.

CZO	21	WWJ	125	CAM	28
RZJ	100	PKZ	60	JVW	132
VWW	90	ZAA	70	ZZX	121

The situation here is not as simple as it was in the preceding problem. If we factor the intervals between repetitions, we find that 5 is a factor of five of the intervals, and 7 is a factor of three. Five would seem to be the right choice but since trigraphic repetitions can occur by accident, we would like some additional evidence.

What we can do to get such evidence is to write out the message in five columns and also in seven columns and see which arrangement produces columns whose distributions seem more likely to be mono-alphabetic.

Without presenting the detailed arithmetic, we give the results of these calculations. The indices of coincidence are:

5 alphabets		7 alphabets	
1	.052	1	.047
2	.064	2	.040
		3	.037
3	.070	4	.047
4	.074	5	.053
		6	.051
5	.068	7	.046
Average index: .066		Average index: .046	

Clearly 5 is a much better choice. In the case of seven alphabets, the columns are unacceptable as monoalphabets. The indices are all low and, in particular, two of the indices are even lower than that of the message as a whole. It is true that one of the indices in the case of five alphabets is low, but in a statistical situation such things can happen. A larger than proportionate share of low frequency letters may have happened to fall in that column. Additionally, the average index for all 5 alphabets is excellent while that for 7 alphabets is poor.

It should be observed at this point that the above use of indices of coincidence will make it possible to determine the number of alphabets in a polyalphabetic message even if there are no repetitions at all to suggest the appropriate width (keyword length). For, distributions can be made to correspond to each assumed width and their I.C.'s calculated. If the message is of reasonable length, the correct width will produce monoalphabetic I.C.'s in the individual columns.

We have good indication that our cipher message is a polyalphabet with five alphabets. It must follow that each of the five columns corresponds to a monoalphabet. We list below the distributions that result from these columns.

A B C D E F G H I J K L M N O P Q R S T U V W X Y Z

A B C D E F G H I J K L M N O P Q R S T U V W X Y Z

A B C D E F G H I J K L M N O P Q R S T U V W X Y Z

A B C D E F G H I J K L M N O P Q R S T U V W X Y Z

A B C D E F G H I J K L M N O P Q R S T U V W X Y Z

Since we are not aware of the general system that has been used, we would first try to fit a normal distribution to these alphabets. Such attempts yield no fruitful results. We must assume that the substitution alphabets are mixed. As a very general type of attack on the problem, we could consider the possibility of trying to solve each column separately as a monoalphabet. We know the relative frequencies of the individual letters in their monoalphabets. Further, we have some information about the way letters combine with one another, and we have digraphic frequencies as aids to the distinctions between vowels and consonants. But the task is much more difficult than the situation encountered in Chapter 2. The letters in a single column, and hence enciphered with the same monoalphabet, are not adjacent in the message text. Information about digraphs formed by them with letters from the preceding column must be treated independently from that pertaining to digraphs formed with letters from the following column, since the preceding and following columns are enciphered by different alphabets. Thus we are unable to get any help from such properties as reversals. Nonetheless there is a chance that some text might be derived. If the message were long enough to give good monographic frequencies, some possibilities might be suggested for the decipherment of individual letters. Any probable words or phrases which might be expected in the message could be checked by frequency considerations and by a special type of pattern related to the polyalphabeticity. If a probable word or phrase has letters repeated at an interval of five (or a multiple of five) those letters would be identically enciphered. As examples of such a property consider the possible words

P R E S I D E N̲ T   J O H N̲ S O N
A T O M I̲ C   E N E R G Y   C O M M I S S I̲ O N
T O̲ M O R R O̲ W
A S   S̲ O O N   A S̲

The cipher positions indicated by the underlined letters would have to be the same, or the assumed text could not be correct in a five-alphabet polyalphabet.

There is of course the possibility that more than one message is available. Consider the situation that arises in studying the communications of an organization which is regularly sending messages that can be intercepted. Suppose that the messages all use the same plain sequence. Then, even if every message has its own key, those alphabets which come from the same key letter would match one another and could be combined. In this way the amount of material available for study in individual alphabets could be accumulated and would improve the chances for determining some text. But even under these special circumstances this would be a difficult situation to cope with. What can the cryptanalyst do now?

3.6   Matching alphabets

Let us go back to the Vigenère square concept which we have supposed to underlie the encipherment and think about it for a moment. We are assuming that the system uses a mixed plain sequence and normal cipher sequences. Consider the top two rows within the square and imagine that the letters A and B are both in the keyword.

```
              Plain sequence unknown
. . . . . . . . . . . . . . . . . . . . . . . . . .
A B C D E F G H I J K L M N O P Q R S T U V W X Y Z
B C D E F G H I J K L M N O P Q R S T U V W X Y Z A
```

The plain sequence above the square is unknown and apparently mixed. Suppose we were to rearrange the plain sequence so as to put it into its normal order, as if, for example, the alphabets were to be written in enciphering form. Then the columns within the square would have to be rearranged. But each column would move as a unit. Thus whatever the plain text equivalent of A_c in alphabet A, it is the same as the plain text equivalent of B_c in alphabet B. Similarly B_c in alphabet A has the same plain text equivalent as C_c in alphabet B. Given two cipher letters which are consecutive in the normal alphabet, the first has the same plain equivalent in alphabet A that the second has in alphabet B. True, the equivalent is unknown. Nonetheless, the probability of occurrence of these two cipher letters is the same because both represent the same plain text letter. Suppose then that we change all the letters in alphabet B to their predecessors in the normal alphabet. Such a step is the same as deciphering every letter in alphabet B by the substitution alphabet

```
Plain    A B C D E F G H I J K L M N O P Q R S T U V W X Y Z
Cipher   B C D E F G H I J K L M N O P Q R S T U V W X Y Z A
```

The new cipher letters in alphabet B will have identical plain language equivalents to those of the cipher letters in alphabet A. Otherwise stated, alphabet B will have been reduced to alphabet A. The frequency distributions for these two cipher alphabets should match each other, since they correspond to the same set of plain language frequencies.

Now the effect of this reduction (of cipher alphabet B to cipher alphabet A) on the B distribution is a shift, one place to the left, of the frequency markings underneath the cipher letters of the B alphabet. For example, if the actual B distribution had been

A B C D E F G H I J K L M N O P Q R S T U V W X Y Z

the shift would produce a new B distribution

A B C D E F G H I J K L M N O P Q R S T U V W X Y Z

With this change the new B distribution will match the original A distribution.

Similar reasoning applies to any two successive alphabets derived from the Vigenère square. If the distribution for the alphabet corresponding to the second key letter is shifted one position to the left it will be reduced to the same monoalphabetic substitution as the alphabet corresponding to the first key letter.

Moreover, this reasoning can be extended. If two rows of the Vigenère square are n apart, then shifting the distribution corresponding to the lower one n places to the left would convert it to the same monoalphabet as is represented by the distribution of the upper alphabet.

But suppose the distance between two rows is unknown. We would not know how many positions of shift are required. However, the correct positioning is distinguishable from all the others by the good match between its distribution and that of the given row. If two distributions match, they result from encipherments by the same monoalphabet. This must mean that the totality of letters in both distributions corresponds to one monoalphabet. Hence if we construct a new distribution by giving to each letter the sum of the frequencies it has in the two original distributions, the result is monoalphabetic.

The way then to determine the right amount of shift between two distributions is to seek the position in which the two distributions match one another. If the message is long and the distributions involve a large number of letters, such matching may actually be accomplished by inspection. It is a matter of setting the distributions opposite one another in such a way that corresponding positions have similar frequencies. High frequencies match high frequencies, low frequencies match low frequencies, etc. in a manner similar to the matching of direct standard alphabets explained in Chapter 1. With practice and experience, one learns to be able to select the right setting by eye. Lacking such experience, or if the number of letters in the distributions is small, the cryptanalyst must find a statistical means to help him make the decision.

If the reasoning is sound, it should be true that one of the possible positions of the two distributions against one another is the correct one. In this position, if we combine the two distributions into one by adding corresponding frequencies, the combined frequencies should correspond to one single monoalphabet. In every other position, the combined frequencies correspond to a polyalphabet of two alphabets. We know that the expected index of coincidence of a two-alphabet distribution is .052, while that of a one-alphabet distribution is .066. Therefore it is expected that the correct positioning will give the highest index of coincidence of all 26 possibilities.

This fact provides a method of procedure. In order to match two of the distributions, we align them in each of the 26 possible positions. For each position we combine the corresponding frequencies and determine the index of coincidence. The largest index of coincidence should determine the correct position.

For each position, the calculation to be performed is the following. Let f_i represent the frequency of the i-th letter in one distribution for which the total number of letters is N. Let f'_i be the frequency of the i-th letter in the second distribution for which the total number of letters is N'. In the combined distribution $f_i + f'_i$ is the frequency of the i-th letter, and the total number of letters is $N + N'$. By our formula for the index of coincidence,

$$\text{I.C.} = \frac{\sum_{i=A}^{i=Z} (f_i + f'_i)(f_i + f'_i - 1)}{(N + N')(N + N' - 1)}.$$

This number is to be calculated for all 26 positions of one distribution against the second.

Since the denominator is constant it is sufficient for comparison purposes to calculate the numerator only. Expanding the numerator we have

$$\sum_{i=A}^{i=Z} (f_i^2 + f_i'^2 + 2f_i f_i' - f_i - f_i')$$

$$= \sum_{i=A}^{i=Z} f_i^2 + \sum_{i=A}^{i=Z} f_i'^2 + 2\sum_{i=A}^{i=Z} f_i f_i' - \sum_{i=A}^{i=Z} f_i - \sum_{i=A}^{i=Z} f_i'$$

In the above expression, each of the terms with the exception of the third one is dependent on only one distribution. The numerical value of such a term is consequently independent of the way the two distributions are placed against one another. Therefore in comparing different alignments of the two distributions to see which one yields the largest index, it is sufficient to calculate only the one term $\sum_A^Z f_i f_i'$. (This, of course, reduces very considerably the amount of computation.)

We shall now apply this procedure to the message we are trying to solve, and illustrate the detail for columns 1 and 2. First, we write out the distribution of column 1, preferably on a sheet of cross section paper. And since we are going to do a good deal of arithmetic with the numbers representing the individual frequencies, it will be more convenient to use arabic numbers than tally marks. See Figure 7, page 86. Then on a second sheet of paper, we write out the distribution of column 2. We do this twice on one line in order to allow for sliding the distribution of column 2 against that of column 1. Figure 8, page 86.

We now place the two alphabets under each other so that the A's are lined up (Figure 9, p. 86), multiply corresponding frequencies and add all the products:

$$\sum_{i=A}^{i=Z} f_i f_i' = 3(2) + 4(2) + 5(1) + \cdots + 0(2) + 5(6).$$

The result is 158.

COL. 1

A	B	C	D	E	F	G	H	I	J	K	L	M	N	O	P	Q	R	S	T	U	V	W	X	Y	Z
3	4	5	1	3	2	1	0	2	0	0	0	5	4	0	4	1	1	6	1	3	6	0	4	0	5

Figure 7

COL. 2

A	B	C	D	E	F	G	H	I	J	K	L	M	N	O	P	Q	R	S	T	U	V	W	X	Y	Z
2	2	1	1	2	1	0	0	0	1	0	0	0	4	1	5	6	1	4	0	4	1	5	2	2	6

Figure 8

COL. 1

A	B	C	D	E	F	G	H	I	J	K	L	M	N	O	P	Q	R	S	T	U	V	W	X	Y	Z
3	4	5	1	3	2	1	0	2	0	0	0	5	4	0	4	1	1	6	1	3	6	0	4	0	5

COL. 2

A	B	C	D	E	F	G	H	I	J	K	L	M	N	O	P	Q	R	S	T	U	V	W	X	Y	Z
2	2	1	1	2	1	0	0	0	1	0	0	0	4	1	5	6	1	4	0	4	1	5	2	2	6

Figure 9

COL. 1

A	B	C	D	E	F	G	H	I	J	K	L	M	N	O	P	Q	R	S	T	U	V	W	X	Y	Z
3	4	5	1	3	2	1	0	2	0	0	0	5	4	0	4	1	1	6	1	3	6	0	4	0	5

COL. 2

B	C	D	E	F	G	H	I	J	K	L	M	N	O	P	Q	R	S	T	U	V	W	X	Y	Z	A
2	1	1	2	1	0	0	0	1	0	0	0	4	1	5	6	1	4	0	4	1	5	2	2	6	2

Figure 10

Next we shift the second alphabet one place to the left so its B is under the A of the first alphabet (Figure 10, page 86) and carry out the same kind of calculation. The result is 129.

We then shift the second alphabet another space to the left and calculate $\sum_{A}^{Z} f_i f_i'$. We continue this process until we have made the calculation for all 26 positions of one alphabet against the other. The complete set of results is given below for each position of the second alphabet relative to the first.

$$\sum_{i=A}^{i=Z} f_i f_i' \text{ for A of alphabet 1 against the indicated letter of}$$
alphabet 2

A	158	N	138
B	129	O	161
C	161	P	138
D	122	Q	115
E	139	R	172
F	136	S	129
G	100	T	122
H	169	U	185
I	126	V	136
J	124	W	149
K	187	X	234
L	87	Y	97
M	161	Z	152

The result for X of alphabet 2 lined up under A of alphabet 1 stands out as the largest number. In this position alphabet 2 has been shifted 23 places to the left.

We now continue by matching the distribution of column 2 against that of column 3, then 3 against 4, and 4 against 5. The results are tabulated below:

	2 vs. 3	3 vs. 4	4 vs. 5
A	190	187	146
B	150	86	125
C	146	148	129
D	140	164	127
E	111	165	105
F	162	117	224
G	94	82	72
H	174	231	118
I	172	122	191
J	108	110	170
K	145	143	122
L	131	109	87
M	91	150	162
N	268	228	123
O	117	53	171
P	111	180	116
Q	180	146	115
R	104	103	146
S	174	206	159
T	110	108	74
U	101	124	177
V	133	190	138
W	165	113	154
X	142	124	152
Y	148	141	71
Z	111	124	197

In the cases of 2 vs. 3, and 4 vs. 5, the right answers are evident because the maximum value of $\sum f_i f_i'$ is considerably larger than all others. But in 3 vs. 4 we have two numbers, 231 and 228, so nearly equal that no clear choice can be made between them.

The occurrence of such an ambiguity is not entirely unexpected. The conclusions we wish to draw from the calculations we have just made are based on statistical arguments. The 25 wrong positions of one alphabet against a second yield results which vary (according to statistical laws) about an average corresponding to an index of coincidence of .052 (the I.C. for two alphabets). If our message is long enough to reflect the statistical findings, i.e. if there is a sufficient number of letters in each distribution, the correct answer, corresponding to an index of .066, will be beyond the farthest extent of the spread of the wrong answers. In other words, if the cipher message is long enough, the correct answer will always be easily distinguishable as belonging to the greatest by far of the 26 calculated results. If the message is not long enough to ensure such a separation between the right answer and the highest wrong ones, ambiguities such as we have just experienced may result. It may even happen in some cases that a wrong positioning gives a bigger number $\sum f_i f'_i$ than the right one.

How do we determine which of the two favorable positions of alphabet 4 against alphabet 3 is, in fact, correct? Note that so far, we have matched the distribution corresponding to each of our columns only against that of an adjacent column. We have not matched 1 and 4, nor 2 and 4, although such matchings might have avoided the ambiguity facing us now. Actually, it is not necessary to do all these matchings because we need to pick the correct position only from 2, not from 26, candidates. To this end we make use of the already determined correct positions of alphabet 1 relative to alphabet 2 and of alphabet 3 relative to alphabet 2, thus inducing the correspondence between alphabets 1 and 3 which can be read off from the first and third lines of the table below:

```
      1:  |A| B C D E F G H I J K L M N O P Q R S T U V W X Y Z
      2:   X Y Z |A| B C D E F G H I J K L M N O P Q R S T U V W
      3:   K L M N O P Q R S T U V W X Y Z |A| B C D E F G H I J
 (i)  4:  |R| S T |U| V W X Y Z A B C D E F G |H| I J K L M N O P Q
 (ii) 4:  |X| Y Z |A| B C D E F G H I J K L M |N| O P Q R S T U V W
```

We now use only the two favorable possibilities
  (i) A in 3 corresponds to H in 4,
  (ii) A in 3 corresponds to N in 4,
(see last 2 lines of table above) and test the induced positions of alphabet 4 relative to alphabet 1,
  (i) A in 1 corresponds to R in 4,
  (ii) A in 1 corresponds to X in 4,
and the two positions of alphabet 4 relative to alphabet 2
  (i) A in 2 corresponds to U in 4,
  (ii) A in 2 corresponds to A in 4.

The calculations of $\sum f_i f'_i$ for alphabets 1 and 4 yield 225 for position (i) and 169 for (ii); those for alphabets 2 and 4 yield the inconclusive result 228 for position (i) and 228 for position (ii).

If we are still not convinced that (i) yields the correct position for alphabet 4 relative to 3, we can check 3 against 5, using our knowledge of the correct position of 4 against 5. The candidates (i) and (ii) yield the values 269 and 156 respectively for $\sum f_i f'_i$, confirming our previous belief that (i) is correct. We now have all the correct positions for the matching of our five distributions.

It is interesting to observe that the initial matching of alphabets could have been done by matching alphabet 1 against alphabets 2, 3, 4, 5 in turn. If the reader carries out these calculations he will find that in those instances all the correct positions are determinable without any ambiguities. Such a result, i.e. no ambiguities, is what we would generally expect whenever the message is sufficiently long to provide strong statistical results.

If there are doubts about some of the answers, then as we have seen, it may prove necessary to test some alphabets against more than one of the others.

The need for such added matching tests suggests a more general type of attack. Instead of trying to match one alphabet against another in the various possible combinations of pairs of alphabets, it would be more systematic to test every alphabet against every other in all possible positions. If there are five alphabets, ten different sets of computations would be carried out. From these the positioning which gives the best fit for each alphabet against all the other four would be selected, and the correct relative settings of all five alphabets could be determined.

An effective modification of this idea would be the following. Suppose we pick from the ten tests just described, a pair of distributions for which the correct result seems certain—i.e. one in which the highest $\sum f_i f'_i$ far exceeds all the others. In our example, we might choose 2 vs. 3 where the value 268 for the N-alphabet is almost half again as large as the second highest value of $\sum f_i f'_i$.

Then combine distributions 2 and 3 by aligning them in the position just chosen

```
2:  A B C D E F G H I  J K L M N  O  O P Q R S T U V W X Y Z
    2 2 1 1 2 1 0 0 0 10 0 0 4 1  5  6 1 1 4 0 4 1 5 2 2 6

3:  N O P Q R S T U V  W  X Y Z A B C D E F G H I J K L M
    1 6 0 3 2 0 0 0 1 11 3 0 6 1 3 3 0 2 5 0 3 0 2 5 0 4
```

and add the corresponding frequencies. The result is a new distribution which we shall call 2 + 3. This new distribution would have the following frequencies:

2+3:	A	B	C	D	E	F	G	H	I	J	K	L	M	N	O	P	Q	R	S	T	U	V	W	X	Y	Z
	3	8	1	4	4	1	0	0	1	21	3	0	10	2	8	9	1	3	9	0	7	1	7	7	2	10

Now match this combined distribution against 1, 4, 5 in turn, and select the outstanding answer, which turns out to be distribution 5 at position Z against A of distribution 2 + 3. Add the frequencies of 5 to those of 2 + 3 to get a combination 2 + 3 + 5. Continuing in this way, the alignment of all the alphabets can be determined. The advantage of this procedure is that the increasingly larger distributions obtained by successive combinations provide for more effective statistical results.

We shall not reproduce the details of these calculations but leave them to the reader as an exercise. It is suggested that he work through the complete process to get an appreciation of how the results are obtained. Obviously the procedures described call for a considerable amount of computational work much of which could be called drudgery, but has to be done. Fortunately it can be eased with the aid of calculating machines or high speed computers.

It is of course possible that a message under study may not be long enough for the alphabets to be matched by any of these procedures. In such a case, and if it is not possible to insert any plain text into the message due to knowledge of the subject matter, or by any other means, it may not be possible to arrive at a merging of alphabets.

What have we accomplished with the message we are trying to solve? We have aligned the 5 alphabets of our original message against one another so that their distributions match. This matching is based, of course, on the assumption that the cipher sequences in the Vigenère square are normal sequences. But how can we be sure that that assumption is a valid one? Can we get any further confirmation of these results?

One kind of confirmation presumably has come from the calculations we have just completed, viz. in the way the highest answer stood out among the sums of the cross-products. If the distributions had not really matched one another in any position, the quantity

$\sum f_i f'_i$ would not consistently have been outstandingly high. But there is a further important check. If we align the distributions in the matching positions that we have determined by these calculations and add all the corresponding frequencies, the resulting distribution should be a monoalphabet. Let us make this check.

The final positioning of the alphabets is shown here—with the frequencies indicated.

```
1: A B C D E F G H I J K L   M N O P Q R S T U V W X Y Z
   3 4 5 1 3 2 1 0 2 0 0 0   5 4 0 4 1 1 6 1 3 6 0 4 0 5

2: X Y Z A B C D E F G H I   J K L M N O P Q R S T U V W
   2 2 6 2 2 1 1 2 1 0 0 0   10 0 0 4 1 5 6 1 1 4 0 4 1 5

3: K L M N O P Q R S T U V   W X Y Z A B C D E F G H I J
   5 0 4 1 6 0 3 2 0 0 0 1   11 3 0 6 1 3 3 0 2 5 0 3 0 2

4: R S T U V W X Y Z A B C   D E F G H I J K L M N O P Q
   7 2 1 1 3 3 1 0 7 0 0 2   7 1 0 2 1 1 8 0 0 5 0 7 0 1

5: W X Y Z A B C D E F G H   I J K L M N O P Q R S T U V
   3 3 5 2 5 0 1 0 4 0 0 0   7 1 0 7 1 3 2 0 2 9 0 2 0 3
```

Figure 11

We observe, incidentally, the word ROBIN down one column of this array; it is possibly the keyword for the message we are trying to solve.

Combining the frequencies of all the letters in each column and placing the results under alphabet 1, we have

```
 A  B  C  D E  F G H I  J K L M  N O  P Q R  S  T U  V W X  Y Z
20 11 21  7 19 6 7 4 14 0 0 3 40 9 0 23 5 13 25 2 8 29  0 20 1 16
```

The total number of letters listed in this combined distribution is 303. We note with satisfaction that the highest frequency—40—is just over 13%, and that there are 4 cipher letters which have not appeared at all. The presence of these blanks is encouraging. But most important of all is the determination of the index of coincidence of this merged distribution to confirm that it is monoalphabetic in character. I.C. turns out to be .065 as against an expected value of .066, and we can feel sure now that we are on the right track.

Exercises

48. Find the best matching position of the following two distributions against one another:

```
A B C D E F G H I J K L M N O P Q R S T U V W X Y Z
1 4 2 7 4 1 6 5 0 4 2 0 1 2 0 0 1 2 3 2 0 3 0 0 0 0

A B C D E F G H I J K L M N O P Q R S T U V W X Y Z
0 3 1 2 4 3 0 0 2 0 4 0 0 4 0 0 0 0 0 2 9 5 0 2 9
```

Prove that the combined alphabet resulting from the matched positions has a monoalphabetic index of coincidence.

49. Match the following distributions and prove that the combined alphabet is monoalphabetic.

```
A B C D E F G H I J K L M N O P Q R S T U V W X Y Z
1 1 4 3 0 1 1 1 2 5 0 0 1 1 4 0 0 1 0 2 0 0 1 9 1 10

A B C D E F G H I J K L M N O P Q R S T U V W X Y Z
4 4 0 1 1 1 7 0 0 4 0 2 1 0 5 1 0 0 0 0 6 3 4 3 1
```

50. Do the distributions of problems 48 and 49 come from the same Vigenère square?

3.7 Reduction of a polyalphabetic cipher to a monoalphabet

We have derived a number of important results about our message, but we still have no information about its text. How are we going to decipher the message?

Consider Figure 11 on page 92 in which the relative positioning of the five alphabets is shown. These correspond to the rows of the Vigenère square which are used for encipherment. What is still unknown is the plain sequence. Whatever that sequence may be, we know that the letters in any single column of Figure 11 will all have the same plain language equivalent. To put it differently, if we replace each letter of alphabet 2 by the letter above it in alphabet 1, the new letter in alphabet 2 and that same letter in alphabet 1 will have the same plain text equivalents. Therefore we decipher the letters of alphabet 2 with the substitution alphabet

```
Plain   A B C D E F G H I J K L M N O P Q R S T U V W X Y Z
Cipher  X Y Z A B C D E F G H I J K L M N O P Q R S T U V W
```

That is, we replace each letter in column 2 of the cipher message by the letter above it in the substitution alphabet shown above. When this has been done, column 2 will have been reduced to the same monoalphabet as column 1.

Similarly, we replace the letters of column 3 in the message by the letters above them in the substitution alphabet

```
Plain   A B C D E F G H I J K L M N O P Q R S T U V W X Y Z
Cipher  K L M N O P Q R S T U V W X Y Z A B C D E F G H I J
```

and they will then be reduced to the monoalphabet of column 1. Continuing this process, the entire polyalphabetic message we started with is reduced to a monoalphabet.

Note that this reduction might also be described as follows: Let the plain sequence of a Vigenère square be the same as line 1 of Figure 11. Then "decipher" the original message as a 5-alphabet cipher using the five rows of Figure 11 as the cipher sequences. The result is as follows:

```
SZMSV GSHMR FPMSI XHMPV ZMGMR VMPAZ SCNXN VZMAS VEXAQ
MRVMP ISQGZ ECMDX CCEIE ATGSP USAID XXCSE PFPXI BDMIV
ZBAIM PRVXP URSAI NBAAM CDCXB IREAV ZMAXP VZMSR VSAIE
AIELE MCEVV CMPMC EMNNP XUVZM ZMSVE RMLFM DVMIB AVECV
BMRIS QSNVM PGZED ZAXPU SCVMU FMPSV BPMRG ECCFP MHSEC
VZPXB TZXBV UXRVX NVZMA SVEXA CXDSC VMUFM PSVBP MRGEC
CYMAM SPCQA XPUSC NXPVZ MAMLV NEHMI SQR
```

The long repetitions shown underlined in this converted message provide an interesting confirmation of monoalphabeticity.

Solving this monoalphabet of over 300 letters is readily accomplished. From monographic frequencies it seems evident that $M_c = E_p$, $V_c = T_p$. The frequent cipher trigraph VZM must be THE. The repeated cipher tetragraph ZMSV enters into the patterns SZMSV and VZMZMSV at the start of the message and suggests $S_c = A_p$. With these entries the rest is easy. The resulting plain text is:

```
A HEAT WAVE SPREAD OVER THE WESTERN HALF OF THE
NATION YESTERDAY WHILE COLLIDING WARM AND COOL
AIR PRODUCED THUNDER STORMS AND FUNNEL CLOUDS IN
THE NORTHEAST AND DIXIE LITTLE RELIEF FROM THE
```

HEAT IS EXPECTED UNTIL TUESDAY AFTER WHICH NORMAL
TEMPERATURES WILL PREVAIL THROUGHOUT MOST OF THE
NATION LOCAL TEMPERATURES WILL BE NEARLY NORMAL
FOR THE NEXT FIVE DAYS

With the solution of the monoalphabet, we find that the plain sequence above the Vigenère square is a transposed keyword mixed
sequence based on the word SOLVE, and that the keyword for
encipherment of the message is ROBIN.

3.8 Polyalphabetic ciphers with mixed cipher sequences

We now examine where the weakness lay that permitted the
previous system to be solved. What, for instance, was it that made
the matching of alphabets possible? It was the fact that the cipher
sequence was normal. Because of that fact we found that if two
rows of the Vigenère square are n apart, then the alphabetic interval
between any two letters representing the same plain text in those
two alphabets would also be n. Shifting one of the distributions
against the other the proper number of places would make them
match, and thus the value of n could be determined.

Actually the cipher sequence does not have to be normal for the
application of the techniques that have been described. It may be
any sequence whatever provided, however, that it is known to the
cryptanalyst. The adjustment that would be required in the solution
procedures would be to write out the distributions of the individual
alphabets in the order of the cipher sequence.

But suppose the cipher sequence is unknown. Then it would no
longer be possible to accomplish the matching of distributions. The
cryptanalyst would therefore be denied the essential property which
permitted him to achieve the kind of solution that has just been
demonstrated.

What is the cryptanalyst's situation if he is up against a polyalphabetic message resulting from a Vigenère square based on an
unknown mixed cipher sequence? He can still conclude that the
message is a polyalphabet, and he can determine the number of
alphabets used. He then knows that all the letters in any one column
are in one alphabet, and he can try to obtain plain text by determining

the plain text equivalents of letters in each monoalphabet by the methods discussed on page 82. It is evident that a rather large amount of text is necessary to achieve any results in such a situation. A single, short message in a polyalphabetic system of this kind would have reasonably good security.

Suppose, however, it should happen that many messages are being enciphered in the same general system, i.e. using the same Vigenère square with a mixed cipher sequence. Suppose further that each message has its own keyword for the selection of enciphering alphabets. Then the cryptanalyst could obtain for each message a monoalphabetic distribution for each alphabet. Whenever a key letter is repeated in one or more messages, the cipher distributions in the alphabet corresponding to that key letter represent the same monoalphabet. Thus, repeated key letters can be determined from the fact that the distributions of their alphabets match one another without any shifting.

If enough messages are available for study, the cryptanalyst has the prospect of accumulating a large enough number of letters in some of the alphabets to hope for the successful identification of a few cipher letters on the basis of frequency. Entering these values in all the places where those cipher letters appear may lead to the insertion of some text which, hopefully, may be expanded and built on to produce successful decryption.

This sounds, and is, difficult even in the most favorable circumstances. However, there sometimes are special situations which the cryptanalyst can use to advantage. We proceed to describe one of these with special features of interest. The particular situation is the following.

Suppose it happens that the same message has to be sent to two recipients who have been provided with different keys. To describe, in detail, the cryptanalytic techniques of such a special case we shall illustrate it with an example and show in the cryptanalysis of the example how it is possible to take advantage of the situation encountered.

We suppose that the cryptanalyst has the following two messages sent from the same place at about the same time to two different addressees:

1. WCOAK TJYVT VXBQC ZIVBL AUJNY BBTMT JGOEV GUGAT KDPKV
   GDXHE WGSFD XLTMI NKNLF XMGOG SZRUA LAQNV IXDXW EJTKI
   YAOSH NTLCI VQMJQ FYYPB CZOPZ VOGWZ KQZAY DNTSF WGOVI
   IKGXE GTRXL YOIP

2. TXHHV JXVNO MXHSC EEYFG EEYAQ DYHRK EHHIN OPKRO ZDVFV
   TQSIC SIMJK ZIHRL CQIBK EZKFL OZDPA OJHMF LVHRL UKHNL
   OVHTE HBNHG MQBXQ ZIAGS UXEYR XQJYC AIYHL ZVMQV QGUKI
   QDMAC QQBRB SQNI

By the methods already described of examining repetitions and
I.C.'s of columnar distributions it can be shown that each of these
messages is polyalphabetic, the first one using six alphabets and the
second one, five.

We note a point of particular interest about these messages,
namely that they are of exactly the same length. Suppose we write
them one under the other:

	5		10		15		20		25		30		35		40		45		50

WCOAK TJYVT VXBQC ZIVBL AUJNY BBTMT JGOEV GUGAT KDPKV GDXHE
TXHHV JXVNO MXHSC EEYFG EEYAQ DYHRK EHHIN OPKRO ZDVFV TQSIC

	55		60		65		70		75		80		85		90		95		100

WGSFD XLTMI NKNLF XMGOG SZRUA LAQNV IXDXW EJTKI YAOSH NTLCI
SIMJK ZIHRL CQIBK EZKFL OZDPA OJHMF LVHRL UKHNL OVHTE HBNHG

	105		110		115		120		125		130		135		140		145		149

VQMJQ FYYPB CZOPZ VOGWZ KQZAY DNTSF WGOVI IKGXE GTRXL YOIP
MQBXQ ZIAGS UXEYR XQJYC AIYHL ZVMQV QGUKI QDMAC QQBRB SQNI

In certain positions of the two messages we find the same letters.
Let us write the numerical positions in the text of these identical
letters.

X	C	D	V	Z	A	Q	Q	G	I
12	15	42	45	72	75	102	105	132	135

The numbers show two evident patterns. The first position bearing
identical letters is 12 and every thirtieth position thereafter houses
identical letters. Similarly, the second position having this property
is 15, and so does every thirtieth position after it.

What can this mean? First of all, since one message has six alphabets
and the other five, we note that 30 is the least common multiple of
6 and 5. Suppose both messages had identical plain text (a reasonable

assumption in view of their being the same size and having been sent about the same time). Suppose further that two letters of one keyword also appear in the other. Since position 12 has identical letters in both messages, and since

$$12 \equiv 6 \ (\text{mod } 6), \qquad\qquad 12 \equiv 2 \ (\text{mod } 5),$$

we are led to believe that

alphabet 6 of the first message = alphabet 2 of the second message.

Similarly, since

$$15 \equiv 3 \ (\text{mod } 6), \qquad\qquad 15 \equiv 5 \ (\text{mod } 5),$$

we suspect that

alphabet 3 of the first message = alphabet 5 of the second message.

The fact that $5 \cdot 6 = 30$ implies

$$12 + 30n \equiv \begin{cases} 6 \ (\text{mod } 6) \\ 2 \ (\text{mod } 5) \end{cases}, \qquad 15 + 30n \equiv \begin{cases} 3 \ (\text{mod } 6) \\ 5 \ (\text{mod } 5) \end{cases}$$

$$\text{for } n = 0, 1, 2, \cdots,$$

and thus accounts for the identity of letters in all the positions listed.

How can we verify the correctness of these statements? By checking that the corresponding alphabets match one another. We make the distributions:

Alph. 6   A B C D E F G H I J K L M N O P Q R S T U V W X Y Z
Msg. 1

Alph. 2   A B C D E F G H I J K L M N O P Q R S T U V W X Y Z
Msg. 2

If we combine the distributions and calculate the I.C. of the combined alphabet we get .075.

For the other two alphabets we get

Alph. 3
Msg. 1   A B C D E F G H I J K L M N O P Q R S T U V W X Y Z

Alph. 5
Msg. 2   A B C D E F G H I J K L M N O P Q R S T U V W X Y Z

The I.C. for the combined alphabet in this case is .066.

These values indicate that the combined alphabets are good mono-alphabets. They tend to confirm the inferences that

(a) The messages are identical,
(b) Alphabet 6 of message 1 = alphabet 2 of message 2,
(c) Alphabet 3 of message 1 = alphabet 5 of message 2.

Since it appears that the messages are identical, we can then say by looking at the first letters of the two messages that W_c in alphabet 1 of message 1 has the same plain text equivalent as T_c in alphabet 1, message 2. Similarly C_c in alphabet 2, message 1 represents the same plain letter as X_c in alphabet 2, message 2. Continuing in this way we can write down an equality between the equivalents of two cipher letters, one in message 1, the other in message 2, for each position of the two messages. Let us record the information systematically as follows. (See Figure 12, page 100). We set up a box of nine lines to represent the nine different alphabets. (There are only nine because two alphabets of message 2 are duplicated in message 1.) Then in column 1 we record the information that W_c in (1,1) (alphabet 1, message 1) is equivalent to T_c in (1,2). We have no knowledge of their plain text equivalent, but we do know that it is the same for both letters. In column 2 we record the fact that C_c in (2,1) is equivalent to X_c in (2,2). Continuing in this way, we record all the pairs of cipher letters in appropriate rows, remembering of course that message 1 has 6 alphabets and message 2 has 5.

A letter of message 1 will be placed on row $(r,1)$ if its position number is of the form $6k + r$; a letter of message 2 will be placed on row $(s,2)$ if its position number is of the form $5k + s$. Figure 12 shows the listings for the first 50 letters; it also shows that when $r = 3$, $s = 5$, identical rows are used to represent the identical alphabets $(3,1)$ and $(5,2)$; and similarly for $r = 6$, $s = 2$.

We can now combine some of these listings as follows. Since the cipher letters in any one row are all from the same alphabet, a repe-

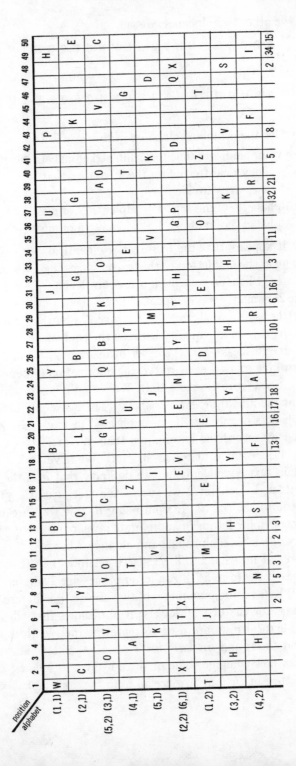

Figure 12

tition in a row must correspond to a repeated plain text letter. Thus, column 7 which has an X in (2,2) must be headed by the same plain letter as column 2 which also has an X in (2,2). As a result of this identity of plain letters, the two columns can be combined into one containing the three letters J, C, X in rows (1,1) (2,1) and (2,2).

In the same way, column 9 can be combined with column 5 because both have a V on the third row and hence both columns represent the same plain text letter. The continuation of this procedure leads to the column identities indicated beneath the box and reduces the number of columns. At the same time, it produces an increasing number of entries in some of the columns. For example, columns 3, 10, 13, 19 combine to give

(1,1)	B
(2,1)	
(3,1)	O
(4,1)	T
(5,1)	
(6,1)	
(1,2)	
(3,2)	H
(4,2)	F

and a check on this information is obtained in column 33 which confirms the O and H.

The process of listing columns and combining them can of course be continued throughout the entire length of the two cipher messages. We shall leave it to the reader to develop the details. The end result, after all the material available has been utilized, is shown in Figure 13.

	A	B	C	D	E	F	G	H	I	J	K	L	M	N	O	P	Q	R	S	T	U	V	W	X	Y	Z	1	2	3	4	5	6	7
(1,1)	W	J	B		D	P		M		N	U	X		L			H	Y		R						T			Z	K	O		
(2,1)	Q	C	K	X		Y		E		A	L		B		G		T			U		V			J								
(3,1)	L	A	O	V	K	W	N	C		Z	G		S	B			Q				F	I	J		E			R					
(4,1)	G	Z	T	F			A	U	X	I						E	L							S									
(5,1)	Y	M	D	K	F		V	R	I	J	W						S				A				H			O					P
(6,1)	I	X	Q	D	T			Z	E	V	P	N		Y	H		G	F			J			K			B						
(1,2)	T	E		Z	J	S	M	U		C	Q	H	D							X	L									A			
(3,2)	J	S	H		V	I	B		Y	N			A	K		M		D							E						U		
(4,2)	S	R	F	N		G		H		M	Y	A	Q			B	J		P		K			T		X							I

Figure 13

The usefulness of this display should be clear. All the letters in any one column represent the same plain text. If we put arbitrary equivalents at the heads of the individual columns, and decipher the message to those equivalents, it will be nearly reduced to a monoalphabet. We have to say "nearly" because we have 33 columns in our display and will therefore have 33 different characters in the reduced message.

If we label the 33 columns in order A, $\cdots$, Z, 1, 2, $\cdots$, 7 as shown in Figure 13 we get the following decipherment:

```
ABCHD EBFDC GBCAH BIJCK BIJLQ MNCBE BOC7G QKOBC DDFCD
ACB7H FAQRE DACBA JCGQE BHOCA QHSTB QUCJV WJCBA HXCDA
QJCYZ L1KHK GCH2Q DANFM HB3K4 VCAKH 5AJHA DJQMD KQ6VO
KDQLH KCHBN FCK7
```

Some of these 33 characters are equal. The text of the original message was not long enough to yield all the identities, and so we have, in effect, what is known as a monoalphabetic substitution with variants. Otherwise stated, some of the columns in Figure 13 should be merged. But these mergings must introduce no conflicts. We can say that columns A, B, C, H, J, K, Q have no variants, because if any one of these were merged with another column, 2 different letters would occupy the same space. The only possible variants of D are S and 6, because the latter two columns are the only ones which have entries only in the rows where column D has vacancies, namely (1,1) and (3,2). A number of other similar statements can be made about possible equivalents and would be of some assistance in trying to solve the monoalphabet.

We recommend to the reader the experiment of solving the reduced cipher. It will not be discussed here because it is possible, by other means, to develop information about the missing identities and so combine additional columns in our deciphering box. We have not yet made full utilization of the possibility that the message was enciphered with the aid of a Vigenère square. We shall now suppose that it has been so enciphered, and shall examine how we can profit from such an assumption.

What we shall do is to establish some useful general properties of Vigenère squares. Consider the most general case of a Vigenère square, one which uses a mixed cipher sequence and a mixed plain sequence. By way of illustration let us use the keyword sequence based on NEW YORK CITY as the plain sequence, and the transposed keyword mixed sequence based on the word CHICAGO as the cipher sequence. The resulting Vigenère square is shown in Figure 14 below. As always in a Vigenère square, any row can be obtained from another row by shifting the other a proper number of places.

```
Plain  N E W Y O R K C I T A B D F G H J L M P Q S U V X Z
      ──────────────────────────────────────────────────────
       C B L S Y H D M T Z I E N U A F P V G J Q W O K R X
       B L S Y H D M T Z I E N U A F P V G J Q W O K R X C
       L S Y H D M T Z I E N U A F P V G J Q W O K R X C B
       S Y H D M T Z I E N U A F P V G J Q W O K R X C B L
       Y H D M T Z I E N U A F P V G J Q W O K R X C B L S
       H D M T Z I E N U A F P V G J Q W O K R X C B L S Y
       D M T Z I E N U A F P V G J Q W O K R X C B L S Y H
       M T Z I E N U A F P V G J Q W O K R X C B L S Y H D
       T Z I E N U A F P V G J Q W O K R X C B L S Y H D M
       Z I E N U A F P V G J Q W O K R X C B L S Y H D M T
    C  I E N U A F P V G J Q W O K R X C B L S Y H D M T Z
    i  E N U A F P V G J Q W O K R X C B L S Y H D M T Z I
    p  N U A F P V G J Q W O K R X C B L S Y H D M T Z I E
    h  U A F P V G J Q W O K R X C B L S Y H D M T Z I E N
    e  A F P V G J Q W O K R X C B L S Y H D M T Z I E N U
    r  F P V G J Q W O K R X C B L S Y H D M T Z I E N U A
       P V G J Q W O K R X C B L S Y H D M T Z I E N U A F
       V G J Q W O K R X C B L S Y H D M T Z I E N U A F P
       G J Q W O K R X C B L S Y H D M T Z I E N U A F P V
       J Q W O K R X C B L S Y H D M T Z I E N U A F P V G
       Q W O K R X C B L S Y H D M T Z I E N U A F P V G J
       W O K R X C B L S Y H D M T Z I E N U A F P V G J Q
       O K R X C B L S Y H D M T Z I E N U A F P V G J Q W
       K R X C B L S Y H D M T Z I E N U A F P V G J Q W O
       R X C B L S Y H D M T Z I E N U A F P V G J Q W O K
       X C B L S Y H D M T Z I E N U A F P V G J Q W O K R
```

Figure 14

Let us now rearrange the substitution alphabets so that they will be in the form of enciphering alphabets. This is accomplished by making the plain sequence normal. Thus we would put the column headed by A first, the column headed by B next, etc. The square would now take the form shown in Figure 15, page 104.

Plain	A	B	C	D	E	F	G	H	I	J	K	L	M	N	O	P	Q	R	S	T	U	V	W	X	Y	Z
	I	E	M	N	B	U	A	F	T	P	D	V	G	C	Y	J	Q	H	W	Z	O	K	L	R	S	X
	E	N	T	U	L	A	F	P	Z	V	M	G	J	B	H	Q	W	D	O	I	K	R	S	X	Y	C
	N	U	Z	A	S	F	P	V	I	G	T	J	Q	L	D	W	O	M	K	E	R	X	Y	C	H	B
	U	A	I	F	Y	P	V	G	E	J	Z	Q	W	S	M	O	K	T	R	N	X	C	H	B	D	L
	A	F	E	P	H	V	G	J	N	Q	I	W	O	Y	T	K	R	Z	X	U	C	B	D	L	M	S
	F	P	N	V	D	G	J	Q	U	W	E	O	K	H	Z	R	X	I	C	A	B	L	M	S	T	Y
	P	V	U	G	M	J	Q	W	A	O	N	K	R	D	I	X	C	E	B	F	L	S	T	Y	Z	H
	V	G	A	J	T	Q	W	O	F	K	U	R	X	M	E	C	B	N	L	P	S	Y	Z	H	I	D
	G	J	F	Q	Z	W	O	K	P	R	A	X	C	T	N	B	L	U	S	V	Y	H	I	D	E	M
	J	Q	P	W	I	O	K	R	V	X	F	C	B	Z	U	L	S	A	Y	G	H	D	E	M	N	T
C	Q	W	V	O	E	K	R	X	G	C	P	B	L	I	A	S	Y	F	H	J	D	M	N	T	U	Z
i	W	O	G	K	N	R	X	C	J	B	V	L	S	E	F	Y	H	P	D	Q	M	T	U	Z	A	I
p	O	K	J	R	U	X	C	B	Q	L	G	S	Y	N	P	H	D	V	M	W	T	Z	A	I	F	E
h	K	R	Q	X	A	C	B	L	W	S	J	Y	H	U	V	D	M	G	T	O	Z	I	F	E	P	N
e	R	X	W	C	F	B	L	S	O	Y	Q	H	D	A	G	M	T	J	Z	K	I	E	P	N	V	U
r	X	C	O	B	P	L	S	Y	K	H	W	D	M	F	J	T	Z	Q	I	R	E	N	V	U	G	A
	C	B	K	L	V	S	Y	H	R	D	O	M	T	P	Q	Z	I	W	E	X	N	U	G	A	J	F
	B	L	R	S	G	Y	H	D	X	M	K	T	Z	V	W	I	E	O	N	C	U	A	J	F	Q	P
	L	S	X	Y	J	H	D	M	C	T	R	Z	I	G	O	E	N	K	U	B	A	F	Q	P	W	V
	S	Y	C	H	Q	D	M	T	B	Z	X	I	E	J	K	N	U	R	A	L	F	P	W	V	O	G
	Y	H	B	D	W	M	T	Z	L	I	C	E	N	Q	R	U	A	X	F	S	P	V	O	G	K	J
	H	D	L	M	O	T	Z	I	S	E	B	N	U	W	X	A	F	C	P	Y	V	G	K	J	R	Q
	D	M	S	T	K	Z	I	E	Y	N	L	U	A	O	C	F	P	B	V	H	G	J	R	Q	X	W
	M	T	Y	Z	R	I	E	N	H	U	S	A	F	K	B	P	V	L	G	D	J	Q	X	W	C	O
	T	Z	H	I	X	E	N	U	D	A	Y	F	P	R	L	V	G	S	J	M	Q	W	C	O	B	K
	Z	I	D	E	C	N	U	A	M	F	H	P	V	X	S	G	J	Y	Q	T	W	O	B	K	L	R

Figure 15

The twenty-six alphabets produced by this square are the same as those of the original square. But the horizontal relationship between two cipher sequences is no longer evident. The original cipher sequence can no longer be seen in the rows of the square. It is retained though in the columnar sequence because the process of rearrangement to the square with normal plain sequence required shifting complete columns.

Let us select two rows from the square of Figure 15, say the first and fourth.

Plain	A	B	C	D	E	F	G	H	I	J	K	L	M	N	O	P	Q	R	S	T	U	V	W	X	Y	Z
Cipher	I	E	M	N	B	U	A	F	T	P	D	V	G	C	Y	J	Q	H	W	Z	O	K	L	R	S	X
	U	A	I	F	Y	P	V	G	E	J	Z	Q	W	S	M	O	K	T	R	N	X	C	H	B	D	L

Since these rows were three apart in the square it must follow that the two letters of any column are three apart in the original cipher sequence. That means that such columnar pairs are consecutive letters in a decimation at interval three. And it also means that we can determine the complete decimation based on interval 3. We start with the letter I and follow it by U (the letter below I in column A). Then we find U on the upper row and follow it by P; we locate P on the upper row and follow it by J, etc. This continued process of "chaining" will produce the 26 letter sequence

I U P J O X L H T E A V Q K C S D Z N F G W R B Y M

which is readily seen to be the decimation, at interval 3, of the original cipher sequence.

If the two rows we started with had been n apart, the chaining process would have produced the decimation of the original sequence at interval n provided, of course, that n is prime to 26. If n is even, the result will be two sequences of 13 letters each. If n is 13, the result will be 13 pairs of letters. In these two latter situations the derived information is useful but a decimation interval prime to 26 must be determined before a complete sequence of 26 letters can be derived.

The same method of producing a decimated sequence would work if the original Vigenère square had been rearranged to have any plain language sequence whatever. So long as the columns are shifted as complete units, two rows of the square yield, by chaining, a decimation of the original cipher sequence.

The important property possessed by the decimated sequence is that it produces a Vigenère square which is in a special sense equivalent to the original square.

To appreciate the significance of this remark let us examine the Vigenère square based on one of the decimated sequences, say that at interval 3. The square is shown on page 106 (Figure 16).

If we put an appropriate plain sequence above this square we will end up with the same 26 alphabets as were produced by the original Vigenère square. One way to develop such a sequence is to make the first alphabet of this new square the same as the first substitution alphabet of the original square. That is, taking

I U P J O X L H T E A V Q K C S D Z N F G W R B Y M

as a cipher sequence, we find the plain sequence which will produce

Plain

I	U	P	J	O	X	L	H	T	E	A	V	Q	K	C	S	D	Z	N	F	G	W	R	B	Y	M
U	P	J	O	X	L	H	T	E	A	V	Q	K	C	S	D	Z	N	F	G	W	R	B	Y	M	I
P	J	O	X	L	H	T	E	A	V	Q	K	C	S	D	Z	N	F	G	W	R	B	Y	M	I	U
J	O	X	L	H	T	E	A	V	Q	K	C	S	D	Z	N	F	G	W	R	B	Y	M	I	U	P
O	X	L	H	T	E	A	V	Q	K	C	S	D	Z	N	F	G	W	R	B	Y	M	I	U	P	J
X	L	H	T	E	A	V	Q	K	C	S	D	Z	N	F	G	W	R	B	Y	M	I	U	P	J	O
L	H	T	E	A	V	Q	K	C	S	D	Z	N	F	G	W	R	B	Y	M	I	U	P	J	O	X
H	T	E	A	V	Q	K	C	S	D	Z	N	F	G	W	R	B	Y	M	I	U	P	J	O	X	L
T	E	A	V	Q	K	C	S	D	Z	N	F	G	W	R	B	Y	M	I	U	P	J	O	X	L	H
E	A	V	Q	K	C	S	D	Z	N	F	G	W	R	B	Y	M	I	U	P	J	O	X	L	H	T
A	V	Q	K	C	S	D	Z	N	F	G	W	R	B	Y	M	I	U	P	J	O	X	L	H	T	E
V	Q	K	C	S	D	Z	N	F	G	W	R	B	Y	M	I	U	P	J	O	X	L	H	T	E	A
Q	K	C	S	D	Z	N	F	G	W	R	B	Y	M	I	U	P	J	O	X	L	H	T	E	A	V
K	C	S	D	Z	N	F	G	W	R	B	Y	M	I	U	P	J	O	X	L	H	T	E	A	V	Q
C	S	D	Z	N	F	G	W	R	B	Y	M	I	U	P	J	O	X	L	H	T	E	A	V	Q	K
S	D	Z	N	F	G	W	R	B	Y	M	I	U	P	J	O	X	L	H	T	E	A	V	Q	K	C
D	Z	N	F	G	W	R	B	Y	M	I	U	P	J	O	X	L	H	T	E	A	V	Q	K	C	S
Z	N	F	G	W	R	B	Y	M	I	U	P	J	O	X	L	H	T	E	A	V	Q	K	C	S	D
N	F	G	W	R	B	Y	M	I	U	P	J	O	X	L	H	T	E	A	V	Q	K	C	S	D	Z
F	G	W	R	B	Y	M	I	U	P	J	O	X	L	H	T	E	A	V	Q	K	C	S	D	Z	N
G	W	R	B	Y	M	I	U	P	J	O	X	L	H	T	E	A	V	Q	K	C	S	D	Z	N	F
W	R	B	Y	M	I	U	P	J	O	X	L	H	T	E	A	V	Q	K	C	S	D	Z	N	F	G
R	B	Y	M	I	U	P	J	O	X	L	H	T	E	A	V	Q	K	C	S	D	Z	N	F	G	W
B	Y	M	I	U	P	J	O	X	L	H	T	E	A	V	Q	K	C	S	D	Z	N	F	G	W	R
Y	M	I	U	P	J	O	X	L	H	T	E	A	V	Q	K	C	S	D	Z	N	F	G	W	R	B
M	I	U	P	J	O	X	L	H	T	E	A	V	Q	K	C	S	D	Z	N	F	G	W	R	B	Y

C
i
p
h
e
r

Figure 16

the alphabet:

```
Plain    A B C D E F G H I J K L M N O P Q R S T U V W X Y Z
Cipher   I E M N B U A F T P D V G C Y J Q H W Z O K L R S X
```

That plain sequence is

```
A F J P U Z W R I B G L Q V N Y K T D H M S X E O C
```

When this newly developed sequence is placed over the Vigenère square based on

```
I U P J O X L H T E A V Q K C S D Z N F G W R B Y M
```

the 26 alphabets obtained are the same as the original 26 alphabets.

However, they do not progress in the same order. If the succession of alphabets produced by the original square is 1, 2, 3, $\cdots$, 26, they appear in the decimated square in the order

$$1, 4, 7, 10, \cdots, 25, 2, 5, \cdots, 23, 26, 3, 6, \cdots 21, 24.$$

So, except for the order in which they appear, the 26 alphabets resulting from a square based on the decimated sequence are the same as those produced by the original square.

If the first square were used to encipher a polyalphabet of r alphabets using r selected rows of the square as determined by the keyword, an appropriate set of r rows from the decimated square would produce exactly the same cipher.

Now suppose that we have somehow determined the correct rows of the decimated square, but we do not know the plain sequence. Choose any plain sequence and decipher the message. The result will be a monoalphabetic encipherment of the original plain text, because all that has been changed are the "names" of the letters at the heads of the columns of the Vigenère square. Thus our methods applied to a decimated square produce results which are monoalphabetic equivalents of the plain text.

Let us return now to our cipher message which we believe is based on a Vigenère square. Except for some gaps and for some variant columns, we have reconstructed the set of correct rows needed to decipher the message. If we had two complete rows we would be able in one chaining operation to produce a decimation of the original cipher sequence. We are not quite in that good a situation, but we can develop portions of a decimated sequence. For example, if we start with rows (3,2) and (4,2) we can conclude that the pairs of letters JS, SR, HF, VG, BH, YM, NY, MB are consecutive in some decimation of the original cipher sequence. Chaining together pairs with a common letter we find that the strings of letters

J S R
N Y M B H F
V G

are all contained in the same decimation. We have no idea what the decimation interval might be. Suppose we call it k.

What we seek to do is to extend these strings using additional information in our box. For example, the decimation interval between (1,1) and (3,2) must be k because those two rows contain the vertical pairs JS, BH, MB, NY and YM. Therefore WJ, PV, UN, LA, RD, OU can be added to the information we already have and used to produce

```
W J S R D
O U N Y M B H F
P V G
L A
```

Now look at rows (1,2) and (1,1) in that order. Since they contain the pairs JD, UM, OY, the decimation interval between them must be $3k$. A pair of letters from (1,2) and (1,1), in that order, must be three apart in the sequence of interval k. Therefore, in terms of interval k, we have

T..W,   E..J,   S..P,   C..N,   Q..U,   H..X,   A..K

In the string W J S R D, we put T three places in front of W, E three places in front of J and P three places beyond S, getting

T E . W J S R D P

We already have the string P V G and can combine it with the string ending with P:

T E . W J S R D P V G

Also C, Q and X may be added to the string beginning O U to give

Q C O U N Y M B H F . X

And the A . . K joins onto L A to give

L A . . K

Now we note rows (1,1) and (4,1). The sequences WG, NX must be from the decimation interval $7k$ because those pairs are letters which are 7 apart in our sequences of interval k. Then

JZ, BT, MA, UI, HE, YL must be seven apart in the sequence of decimation k. With these pairs, the partial sequences so far put together can be merged into

T E K W J S R D P V G Z Q C O U N Y M B H F I X L A

and we have the complete sequence of decimation k.

With this sequence determined, it becomes possible to fill in completely the box giving the columns from the Vigenère square. We begin with the first two rows, (1,1) and (2,1). We note that W and Q, in column 1, are 9 apart in the sequence. Therefore the two entries in any column of those two rows must be 9 apart. So the letter above X of the second row must be O; the letter in row 2 below D in the first row must be N; the letter below X in the first row must be R, etc. In any column of rows 1 and 2 where one letter is known, the second can be filled in from the known decimated sequence. When this has been done, the fourth column can be merged with the next-to-last and the two columns with R in row (1,1) can be merged, as can the two columns with T in row (1,1) (see table below).

(1,1)	W	J	B	O	D	P		M		N	U	X	G	L	E	H	Y		R	R		T					T	F		Z	K	O	
(2,1)	Q	C	K	X	N	Y		E		A	L	R	B	D	G	W	T		U	U		V					V	J		H	Z	X	
(3,1)	L	A	O	V	K	W	N	C		Z	G		S	B		Q			F	I	J			E						R			
(4,1)	G	Z	T	F					A	U	X	I			E	L									S								
(5,1)	Y	M	D	K	F					V	R	I	J	W					S			A				H			O			P	
(6,1)	I	X	Q	D	T					Z	E	V	P	N		Y	H		G	F				J			K			B			
(1,2)	T	E								Z	J	S	M	U	C	Q	H	D			O					X	L					A	
(3,2)	J	S	H							V	I	B		Y	N		A	K	M		D								E			U	
(4,2)	S	R	F	N				G		H		M	Y	A	Q				B	J		P		K			T		X			I	

We then see that rows (2,1) and (3,1) are 12 apart in the sequence. Using this information, we can fill in the missing letter in any column which has just one entry in those two rows.

The continuation of this procedure permits the entire box to be filled in. It is found to reduce to only 21 columns. If we head the columns arbitrarily by 21 letters we can then decipher the original message to these 21 letters, and the result will be a monoalphabetic substitution of the original plain text. We can conclude that the plain text contains only 21 distinct letters. The monoalphabetic message is:

```
ABCHD EBFDC GBCAH BFJCK BFJLQ MNCBE BOC7G QKOBC
DDFCD ACB7H FAQRE DACBA JCGQE BHOCA QHSSB QUCJV
OJCBA HXCDA QJCNS LVKHK GCHGQ DANFM HBVKU VCAKH
RAJHA DJQMD KQDVO KDQLH KCHBN FCK7
```

Its solution is not difficult. The plain text begins TREASURY SECRETARY.

Observe that the mixed sequence reconstructed on page 109 may not have been the original cipher sequence in the Vigenère square. It is, however, a decimation of the original sequence and, for that reason, serves as an equivalent for purposes of decipherment.

If it were desired to determine the original sequence, it would be necessary to write out all the odd decimations (interval 13 only would be omitted) and to examine them to see whether any one of them shows evidence of having been systematically constructed. If such were found, it would be the original sequence. Reconstructing the Vigenère square so that the original cipher sequence appears within it would then produce the original plain sequence above the square.

3.9 General comments about polyalphabetic ciphers

This chapter has discussed the methods by which a polyalphabetic cipher may be recognized and solved. The procedure consists in determining the number of alphabets used and then either solving the alphabets individually or making use of interrelationships between the alphabets to reduce the original cipher to a monoalphabetic cipher. The inherent weakness of a polyalphabetic system lies in the fact that the alphabets used for encipherment are periodically repeated. To remove that weakness, it becomes necessary to use multiple alphabets in a nonrepetitive or aperiodic manner. The study of such aperiodic ciphers is beyond the scope of this text.

Exercises

51. In the problem of identical length messages, on page 97, the existence of common alphabets between the two messages was manifested by the presence of coincidences at certain positions of the two texts. Suppose there were no repeated key letters. How would this be manifested?

52. From the equivalent sequence of page 109, determine the original cipher sequence of the Vigenère square used to encipher the identical messages of page 97. Then determine the original plain sequence. On what keywords are these sequences based?

Solve:

53. UYSMS ZNZGC MBOVF YJVOK SBRNM ISFIA VVGKM QDFAZ YGFIG
    KVRNR YSRTU RLZEL FIGWS EFYCX IFUSI DEGUY SCEZF KWWIZ
    JCZSS ATFTN SYMRF CEEFS SSRTS VHEVA FUHYE ZFIWM EAURL
    ZELFI GNYRU FASWG BBSCG BSISM XRESM DLRNR QRMAF J

54. IHLNO CJBZA ELTGX KGVOA RNRYR WSUTF USWII MDIAL KYMZI
    SQIXK VLVRX ZGNMA LTZGN FBRXZ GNUAG EILVH YRGRE WIYLG
    VAHPR VIREL XBIJK ALCAQ IIVVL RRJKA LWVWC RGKNB WECVB
    LSHAI XTUVQ WZGLZ SHGKK LJBUX JHMMA LTZGN UAGPF HACAJ
    LROLY OEIU

55. ICRGD JAVSQ ISXWJ SIRKD BVVIB QYEHW PIDBP ZUCIS YRRFX
    KTUVT WRWIA BVENX ZERRM QSSGV FVJDT XMTUN ICABY MTDZN
    QZGAI SDRUV KQKFD VDXJS XAVSM EINMS SDYBC LXFBA JNDQO
    TISMV FMDIJ FMBCA ZQGSZ VDIKK EPMIQ GMAQM LJGCM FOREI
    UOICR QGCDS GLRAE ELFHS QDDZL SBDNH QLRUG NVHYN D

56. FWPAY FEALS NVXLO ETAYS XIRHQ XSAHQ OIZES AYVHR GYZWR
    AJNHR NCRYQ BYIHG DYHHC DIRHQ XSAHQ TJJEZ EGKMV LYRHA
    HJVKY ZMXLA NJNHC DIHGS BEFVK XBPHH BYVHR AKPUB IWREA
    EHMWQ NPNHC DCJMO DVEBU OVPSS BEMWQ NVRSA DADWK DDQTN
    PYDSR NIFVK XBPTB MVPKO PPNQY DEYKQ ASQIV FWVAB XSDLO
    AAAIS NSAFY FEALY DMPVD OWUMO AYNIS

57. It is known that the system in which this message was enciphered uses a Vigenère square with the plain sequence normal and the cipher sequence keyword mixed (not transposed) based on the keyword EARTH-QUAKES.

    IPKNE DUSOL SPZVP HAETP WPMYK FKYKP PKNZW SEEZI OLYQC
    QETPL LPUBM CASPJ BCIBF FVPWE BLFSL HOGFL ABKAH MOWJS
    QDBGV HQAVJ QYPBN VWBNP XLMLT PEXOL ADVLN DCOSE WSNSU
    KMEWJ NAZKR VTVDA ZXNAZ JZTOO QFUPZ MXBFX MVQFY QICKT
    BBDBW EKMFM VQNDW JDBLP QFTHE WFSRV WSWVP HAEPA VMUBW
    WLGED XHEFW QUEPY MSLHH BFTNA DTWWA YQWLG WWZ

58. XTDVM IQEUP ZJJZZ OUACA QEUMZ XSEHD RUWXF VLOZK KZBUF
    GCGZN LIWGI KKBDL GYMSS EUJHQ ZOUAC AQEGE UPDTV LOZKK
    ZBUFL GAQSD AONGQ BDVZJ BLQNO ONDRQ NKTMZ PQKRT MKQHJ
    XKNXZ BPEZH EWQLM VAHXK LIWKG KZYOZ XUMED VFJUH BZUBU
    MXGJE FMWMH DKGVR WKXDV ASWXT DVMUM GJRFH ZESSD OPKQR
    JXOGG PRJJF LKKWB VUMSX VAXBJ PFHPK VCGRP KDLPK QXTDV
    AMWBK PONDR VXUOY TFWHK EVTVQ APBUU OVLFZ XDZBU FMUUO
    EUMUX BWBRO W

59. CYLOF XNMNO VVNUN XNIDZ LUOPL XLCCU VXJVG ATRRH ZMSMZ
    RRHZM DXDSB SVBFC ICHPO IEACR HAGIH ZLEML CMAZI FRBBN
    OZBUF AQQLA TBVQD BHCCH LFVYS MZRRH ZMTGP ZKQOU HZIUW
    HMSVK FNORA MQQDO CMNOV VNUZU NQDQI EQFZU RCIUD BNIHF
    NJHEY ASGAJ ORQXT SXBZT KUDZL UODQZ ZOPRH FCYLV UBKIQ
    YGLIB DXYEO QIEDX OIDHM ORAOU DKKSF RBUZS IVCEU NTONM
    RCJIL SYRRA GILVG PKECY LVBYO LDEOC BYHAU ZHVNU VTYQP
    ZBCZT KUWZX CZHDE QVYUZ FJUHC FBDHL XWCYC HPUUL LUBBH
    JCLKC EKTKU WZXCW VJEAS XMHPQ RFAOC VYCEE CPZKK QXBZT
    NDHLQ TMNTH TKUIC PNUXG BH

60. The system in which this message was enciphered used the keywords
    UNDERWATER for the plain sequence and HYDROGRAPHY for
    the cipher sequence; both are transposed keyword mixed.

    AOWNJ ATLXP QMLKV YDDBD IDZBB AJXML OWYSO GJHML BLABT
    JJGMB IWEXJ RDUPV NNXBH RVHPM UFLSD RVUAO STGHU QPTPB
    IWFUP PBHPB IDMAN JQGGL PDWNO YWHKI MWMAN PXAUY FXXLI
    AHGMV YMGOI YRXBQ RZWUQ RXHCI MWINB IWLPB ONZAP PLPUJ
    LNQIV UZLUD UWXNN RAGSB UDQGQ JJGMO OLQOL PRDAP PDXBO
    YZHSL BLABT JJHRP PLRZQ AJLMO ERGSP QOJLB APXAJ BGRXB
    PTGII Y

61. The following two messages were sent to different addresses from the
    same point of origin at approximately the same time. (Hint: If it is
    suspected that the text of one message is identical with a part of the
    other, try juxtaposing the shorter one at the beginning or at the end of
    the longer.)

    Message #1:

    ZSRDQ XHPCZ BYMHS KWHHD HRTQS JTRHH KVOUA JANOK TWOPD
    JCGVL GEOGD UHTIF XUBVG ZSRVH ZVAAG ZEPAG XBPAF ZWASP
    AXFVS TQOAZ BYLEO UXYUS JMOMG BGTPL JQOUS JCTOA REQSF
    HKCTF IQOID HRDBZ PANUX JKRUD HXCTR GVJVW XEPAM JHLBR
    KJPJF QTROL JQOUR UVQUQ RVLGM GCRAM ZSRVR MQAOF BOYHS
    ZSRDB BNBBS JXLSA RKRHE JEOUP JQAMZ XHYEH UXHEW PWOID
    HKFPB TKRAL YHRDA ZAEEH PQEUR JQCVH GTNLZ BVQL

    Message #2:

    XFFST MZYDG YCOVU YXITY XUGCH OKTQV RCTKQ VEWIZ PVQTS
    IZKDU DVOJA HWDAJ MUUYT DSXFZ UGAAD UWVQD OXCUQ QQCNT
    HYPAA RKXCG FTQPF FOQNE OFFIR JNOGZ SKTBA HWDAZ CYIXK
    DTKCT ZJFNE MCZOR FOXYZ DLSDH XCPPC TZCUV QNKFX CGFTI
    OQVTP IOXDQ YWSMK QVEQM ESVTF GZEAW YGFNJ FFZJA YMAHV
    QBFNX HWTZN DBWIO HTXH

CHAPTER FOUR

Polygraphic Systems

4.1 Digraphic ciphers based on linear transformations—matrices

We have seen in the previous chapters that various techniques associated with the frequencies of individual letters and their combinations enable the cryptanalyst to cope with different kinds of substitution ciphers. Conceivably this may remain true even for more sophisticated methods of cryptography so long as the unit of cryptography remains a single letter. Perhaps the way for the cryptographer to prevent the cryptanalyst's successes with letter frequencies might be to make the unit of encipherment a group of letters instead of just one. A system of cryptography in which a group of n plain text letters is replaced as a unit by a group of n cipher letters is called a *polygraphic system*.

In the simplest case, $n = 2$, the system is called *digraphic*. Each pair of plain text letters is replaced by a cipher digraph.

There are many different ways to set up the plain-cipher relationships for a digraphic system. For example, a 26 × 26 square can be constructed with the $26^2 = 676$ possible digraphs entered randomly into the cells of the square. Normal alphabets across the top of the square and down the left side serve as plain language coordinates. The cipher equivalent of the plain digraph P_1P_2 is found in the cell on row P_1 and in column P_2. A portion of such a square is shown on p. 113; the cipher equivalents for AC, BE, CD are RA, AS, YE.

	A	B	C	D	E	F	.	.
A	QX	FN	RA	PD	CO	..	..	..
B	LU	TD	BN	EZ	AS	..	..	..
C	MG	OP	HJ	YE	LB	..	..	..

This square would be difficult to use for decipherment. It would be desirable to construct the inverse square if any reasonable amount of use were anticipated.

A digraphic system of some historical interest was introduced by the English scientist Playfair. A mixed alphabetic sequence of 25 letters (one letter, usually J, is omitted) is written into a square 5 × 5, see Figure 17.

D	B	M	W	I
C	O	X	G	E
Q	Y	R	F	S
Z	A	K	T	P
L	U	H	M	V

Figure 17

The rules for encipherment are:

1. If P_1 and P_2 are two corners of a rectangle, then C_1 and C_2 are the other corners with C_1 on the same row as P_1. *Example*: RE is enciphered as SX.

2. If P_1 and P_2 are on the same row, C_1 and C_2 are to the right of P_1 and P_2. (The first column is considered to be to the right of the last column.) *Example*: GE is enciphered as EC.

3. If P_1 and P_2 are in the same column, C_1 and C_2 are just below P_1 and P_2. (The top row is considered to be just below the bottom row.) *Example*: IS is enciphered as EP.

4. No provision is made for the encipherment of a double letter; if a double letter occurs, a null letter (usually X) is inserted to eliminate the doublet.

Decipherment rules are readily expressed as the inverse of those for encipherment.

From a mathematical point of view, a specially interesting type of polygraphic system is that originally described in the *American Mathematical Monthly* (March, 1931) by Lester S. Hill. The subject of this chapter will be a simplified version of Hill's system.

The fundamental notion employed is that of a linear transformation on n variables. To simplify the exposition, we shall choose $n = 2$ so that our system will be digraphic. (Larger values of n will be discussed later.)

Since the techniques employed are numerical in character, we use a letter-to-number correspondence to permit us to replace each letter by a number. For example, we might assign to each letter the number corresponding to its position in the normal alphabet (see page 5).

The encipherment procedure takes two successive plain text letters P_1 and P_2 at a time and substitutes them (their numerical equivalents) into a pair of congruences (modulo 26) of the form

(4.1)
$$C_1 \equiv aP_1 + bP_2 \quad (\text{mod } 26)$$
$$C_2 \equiv cP_1 + dP_2 \quad (\text{mod } 26),$$

thus determining the cipher equivalent C_1C_2 of the plain text digraph. The process is continued, digraph by digraph, until the entire message has been enciphered. We shall illustrate the method below.

The four numbers a, b, c, d with which the congruences are formed constitute the specific key. They are usually written in the square array, enclosed in large parentheses, called a *matrix*:

$$\begin{pmatrix} a & b \\ c & d \end{pmatrix}.$$

To illustrate the enciphering procedure, we choose the encipherment matrix

$$\begin{pmatrix} 7 & 9 \\ 3 & 12 \end{pmatrix}.$$

Then the congruences are

$$C_1 \equiv 7P_1 + 9P_2 \quad (\text{mod } 26),$$
$$C_2 \equiv 3P_1 + 12P_2 \quad (\text{mod } 26).$$

Suppose the message to be enciphered is:

PREPARE TO EVACUATE AT ONCE

Then the first digraph to be enciphered is PR,

$$P_1 = 16, \qquad P_2 = 18,$$
$$C_1 \equiv 7(16) + 9(18) \equiv 274 \equiv 14 = N,$$
$$C_2 \equiv 3(16) + 12(18) \equiv 264 \equiv 4 = D.$$

The second digraph to be enciphered is EP,

$$P_1 = 5, \qquad P_2 = 16,$$
$$C_1 \equiv 7(5) + 9(16) \equiv 179 \equiv 23 = W,$$
$$C_2 \equiv 3(5) + 12(16) \equiv 207 \equiv 25 = Y.$$

Continuing in this way, the encipherer would get

```
pr ep ar et oe va cu at ea to nc e
ND WY MK GU TA GZ BA EI RA OF UZ
```

Since the message contains an odd number of letters so that a single one is left at the end, the encipherer adds a dummy letter to form a final digraph. Thus if he chooses the letter X, the final cipher digraph would be QQ. The message would now be written in groups of five for transmission:

```
NDWYM KGUTA GZBAE IRAOF UZQQ
```

It is clear that the cipher digraph is a function of both letters in the plain digraph. The fact that two plain text digraphs have one letter in common is in no way discernible in their cipher equivalents, similarly if two cipher digraphs have a letter in common it reveals nothing about the corresponding plain text digraphs. Monographic frequencies have been completely concealed.

Since the encipherment procedure involves a good deal of arithmetic, enciphering a long message could become burdensome. Additionally, care must be exercised to avoid making mistakes. A person doing this kind of work would quickly start wondering whether the process could be simplified.

We will describe one way to accomplish a simplification. The first step is to prepare a scale for P_1 which will consist of two parts. The first part of the scale corresponds to the coefficient of P_1 in the expression for C_1, which in this case is 7. Under the letters of the normal alphabet we write the successive multiples of 7 reduced modulo 26. An easy way to do this is to count by 7's making the modular reductions as required. In other words the counting process is 7, 14, 21, 2, 9, etc. (See Figure 18.) This is, of course, the decimation process on interval 7. The second part of the scale is decimated at interval 3, the coefficient of P_1 in C_2.

P_1:	A	B	C	D	E	F	G	H	I	J	K	L	M
aP_1:	7	14	21	2	9	16	23	4	11	18	25	6	13
cP_1:	3	6	9	12	15	18	21	24	1	4	7	10	13

P_1:	N	O	P	Q	R	S	T	U	V	W	X	Y	Z
aP_1:	20	1	8	15	22	3	10	17	24	5	12	19	26
cP_1:	16	19	22	25	2	5	8	11	14	17	20	23	26

P_2:	A	B	C	D	E	F	G	H	I	J	K	L	M
bP_2:	9	18	1	10	19	2	11	20	3	12	21	4	13
dP_2:	12	24	10	22	8	20	6	18	4	16	2	14	26

P_2:	N	O	P	Q	R	S	T	U	V	W	X	Y	Z
bP_2:	22	5	14	23	6	15	24	7	16	25	8	17	26
dP_2:	12	24	10	22	8	20	6	18	4	16	2	14	26

Figure 18

The scale for P_2 uses decimations 9 and 12 corresponding to the coefficients of P_2 in the expressions for C_1 and C_2. Note that in the latter case we get the 13 even numbers twice each.

To encipher a digraph P_1P_2 with these scales we get C_1 by adding the first number under P_1 to the first number under P_2 and reducing this sum modulo 26. C_2 is obtained by adding the second numbers under P_1 and P_2 and reducing this sum modulo 26.

Thus, to encipher PR, we obtain

$$C_1 \equiv 8 + 6 \equiv 14 = N$$
$$C_2 \equiv 22 + 8 \equiv 30 \equiv 4 = D.$$

Making the scales on separate strips so that they can be slid against one another to put P_2 under P_1 simplifies the look-up procedure.

The cryptographic system must naturally provide a procedure for decipherment. This is accomplished by giving the decipherer a transformation which is the *inverse* of that for encipherment.†

In this particular case, the deciphering transformation is that based on the matrix

$$\begin{pmatrix} 18 & 19 \\ 15 & 17 \end{pmatrix}.$$

To use it, the decipherer treats the cipher message as though it were plain text. The result he derives from his computations is the original message. The reader should confirm the correctness of the deciphering transformation by deciphering some of the cipher digraphs.

We speak of the matrix which enters into our calculations as being 2×2, because it has two rows and two columns. In referring to the elements of a matrix, we use two subscripts, the first indicating the row and the second the column in which the element is contained. Thus the entry on the i-th row and in the j-th column is referred to as m_{ij}. The general 2×2 matrix is written

$$\begin{pmatrix} m_{11} & m_{12} \\ m_{21} & m_{22} \end{pmatrix}.$$

Since we are working in an arithmetic modulo 26, our 4 matrix elements are always from the set $\{1, 2, \cdots, 26\}$.

If two matrices differ in any way, they do not produce identical encipherments. So we say that two matrices are equal if and only if all the corresponding elements are the same. Thus

$$\begin{pmatrix} a_{11} & a_{12} \\ a_{21} & a_{22} \end{pmatrix} = \begin{pmatrix} b_{11} & b_{12} \\ b_{21} & b_{22} \end{pmatrix}$$

if and only if $a_{11} = b_{11}$, $a_{12} = b_{12}$, $a_{21} = b_{21}$, $a_{22} = b_{22}$.

How is the deciphering transformation calculated from the given

† How the deciphering matrix is obtained from the given enciphering matrix will be described shortly.

enciphering transformation? It comes essentially from the process of solving, for P_1 and P_2, the congruences

$$C_1 \equiv 7P_1 + 9P_2$$
$$C_2 \equiv 3P_1 + 12P_2.$$

Thus, if we multiply the first congruence by 4, and the second by 3, we make the coefficients of P_2 the same in both congruences.

$$4C_1 \equiv 28P_1 + 36P_2$$
$$3C_2 \equiv 9P_1 + 36P_2.$$

Subtracting the lower congruence from the upper, we obtain

$$4C_1 - 3C_2 \equiv 19P_1 \equiv 4C_1 + 23C_2.$$

To solve for P_1 we must now divide by 19, or what is equivalent, we must multiply by the reciprocal of 19 (mod 26). Such a reciprocal exists since 19 is prime to 26 (see Chapter 1, p. 26). It is the solution of the congruence

$$19x \equiv 1 \pmod{26}.$$

We have already seen (pp. 25–26) that the solution of this congruence is $x = 11$. So we multiply both sides of

$$19P_1 \equiv 4C_1 + 23C_2$$

by 11 and get

$$209P_1 \equiv 44C_1 + 253C_2$$

which reduces to

$$P_1 \equiv 18C_1 + 19C_2.$$

Substituting the value of P_1 into the original congruence for C_1, we obtain

$$C_1 \equiv 7P_1 + 9P_2$$
$$\equiv 7(18C_1 + 19C_2) + 9P_2$$
$$\equiv 126C_1 + 133C_2 + 9P_2,$$
$$9P_2 \equiv 5C_1 + 23C_2.$$

Now to divide by 9, we multiply by 3 (the reciprocal of 9 modulo 26) and reduce:

$$P_2 \equiv 15C_1 + 17C_2.$$

The linear transformation for the decipherment is

$$P_1 \equiv 18C_1 + 19C_2$$
$$P_2 \equiv 15C_1 + 17C_2,$$

and its matrix is

$$\begin{pmatrix} 18 & 19 \\ 15 & 17 \end{pmatrix}.$$

As we have already seen, this transformation will decipher the cipher message that had been prepared.

The newly calculated matrix

$$\begin{pmatrix} 18 & 19 \\ 15 & 17 \end{pmatrix}$$

is called *the inverse* of the matrix

$$\begin{pmatrix} 7 & 9 \\ 3 & 12 \end{pmatrix}$$

modulo 26 since the transformation corresponding to the former will decipher messages enciphered by the latter.

A word of caution must be inserted here. In calculating the inverse matrix we encountered the requirement of dividing by 19 to get P_1, and by 9 to get P_2. These were both possible operations, since 19 and 9 are both prime to 26 and hence have reciprocals modulo 26. But suppose it had been necessary to divide by a number which has no reciprocal modulo 26, as, for example, any even number. Then it would not have been possible to solve for P_1 and P_2. In such a case, our enciphering process would have had no corresponding decipherment, and the enciphering transformation would not be acceptable.

The consequence is that we cannot choose our enciphering matrix at random. It must be chosen so as to have an inverse. We shall elaborate on this question in the next section.

Exercises

62. Decipher the message

YITJP GWJOW FAQTQ XCSMA ETSQU SQAPU SQGKC PQTYJ

using the deciphering matrix $\begin{pmatrix} 5 & 1 \\ 2 & 7 \end{pmatrix}$

63. Decipher the message

MWALO LIAIW WTGBH JNTAK QZJKA ADAWS SKQKU AYARN CSODN
IIAES OQKJY B

using the deciphering matrix $\begin{pmatrix} 2 & 23 \\ 21 & 7 \end{pmatrix}$

4.2 Multiplication of matrices—inverses

Let us examine how we can guarantee the existence of an inverse. For this purpose we first look at the following question. What result is obtained if one transformation is followed by a second? That is the same as asking, what result is obtained if a message is enciphered with one matrix and the result is then enciphered with a second matrix?

This is not difficult to determine. If the first matrix is

$$A = \begin{pmatrix} a_{11} & a_{12} \\ a_{21} & a_{22} \end{pmatrix},$$

the pair $P_1 P_2$ of plain letters will be replaced by the pair $C_1 C_2$ of cipher letters according to the congruences

(4.2)
$$\begin{aligned} C_1 &\equiv a_{11}P_1 + a_{12}P_2 \\ C_2 &\equiv a_{21}P_1 + a_{22}P_2. \end{aligned}$$

The second matrix

$$B = \begin{pmatrix} b_{11} & b_{12} \\ b_{21} & b_{22} \end{pmatrix}$$

applied to the resulting cipher will yield

$$C_1' \equiv b_{11}C_1 + b_{12}C_2$$
$$C_2' \equiv b_{21}C_1 + b_{22}C_2.$$

We substitute the expressions (4.2) for C_1 and C_2 to obtain

$$C_1' \equiv b_{11}(a_{11}P_1 + a_{12}P_2) + b_{12}(a_{21}P_1 + a_{22}P_2)$$
$$C_2' \equiv b_{21}(a_{11}P_1 + a_{12}P_2) + b_{22}(a_{21}P_1 + a_{22}P_2).$$

Multiplying and collecting like terms, we obtain

$$C_1' \equiv (b_{11}a_{11} + b_{12}a_{21})P_1 + (b_{11}a_{12} + b_{12}a_{22})P_2$$
$$C_2' \equiv (b_{21}a_{11} + b_{22}a_{21})P_1 + (b_{21}a_{12} + b_{22}a_{22})P_2.$$

The two successive encipherments could have been produced in one operation by the matrix

$$\begin{pmatrix} b_{11}a_{11} + b_{12}a_{21} & b_{11}a_{12} + b_{12}a_{22} \\ b_{21}a_{11} + b_{22}a_{21} & b_{21}a_{12} + b_{22}a_{22} \end{pmatrix} = BA$$

which is called the *product* $B \cdot A$ of the matrices A and B. Note how this matrix could have been obtained from the two original matrices. The term in the i-th row and the j-th column of the product is the result of going across the i-th row of the matrix B and down the j-th column of the matrix A, multiplying corresponding terms and adding the products.

Example:

Multiply $\begin{pmatrix} 1 & 2 \\ 3 & 5 \end{pmatrix}$ by $\begin{pmatrix} 5 & 6 \\ 7 & 3 \end{pmatrix}$.

Answer:

$$\begin{pmatrix} 1 & 2 \\ 3 & 5 \end{pmatrix}\begin{pmatrix} 5 & 6 \\ 7 & 3 \end{pmatrix} = \begin{pmatrix} 1(5) + 2(7) & 1(6) + 2(3) \\ 3(5) + 5(7) & 3(6) + 5(3) \end{pmatrix}$$

$$\equiv \begin{pmatrix} 19 & 12 \\ 24 & 7 \end{pmatrix} \quad (\text{mod } 26).$$

We note here that the order of multiplication is important. If we reverse the order of the matrices in our example and multiply

$$\begin{pmatrix} 5 & 6 \\ 7 & 3 \end{pmatrix} \quad \text{by} \quad \begin{pmatrix} 1 & 2 \\ 3 & 5 \end{pmatrix}, \quad \text{the result is} \quad \begin{pmatrix} 23 & 14 \\ 16 & 3 \end{pmatrix},$$

quite different from the result of the previous multiplication. This is a kind of multiplication in which, in general,

$$A \cdot B \neq B \cdot A.$$

Such a type of multiplication is said to be *non-commutative*.

We now use our understanding of multiplication of matrices to examine under what circumstances a transformation has an inverse.

If the matrix B is the inverse of a given matrix A, then the transformation with B should undo the work of the transformation with A; that is, after performing the A-transformation, followed by the B-transformation, we should end up with the original plain letters, in other words, with

$$C_1' \equiv P_1$$
$$C_2' \equiv P_2.$$

If we write these equations in the form

$$C_1' \equiv P_1 + 0 \cdot P_2$$
$$C_2' \equiv 0 \cdot P_1 + P_2,$$

we see that the corresponding matrix is

$$\begin{pmatrix} 1 & 0 \\ 0 & 1 \end{pmatrix} = I.$$

Since it produces an encipherment in which each pair $P_1 P_2$ is replaced by itself ($P_1 \equiv C_1'$, $P_2 \equiv C_2'$), this matrix is called the *identity matrix* and denoted by I; it always leads to the identity transformation in which each pair is replaced by itself, no matter what the modulus is.

It is not difficult to show that, if $B \cdot A = I$, then also $A \cdot B = I$; in other words, a matrix commutes with its inverse.

We have shown so far: *Two matrices A and B are inverses of each other if their product is the identity matrix.* This, applied to our work, means: An enciphering transformation

$$C_1 \equiv a_{11}P_1 + a_{12}P_2$$
$$C_2 \equiv a_{21}P_1 + a_{22}P_2$$

has a corresponding deciphering transformation if the matrix

$$A = \begin{pmatrix} a_{11} & a_{12} \\ a_{21} & a_{22} \end{pmatrix}$$

has an inverse. To illustrate this principle, we multiply the matrices we have used for encipherment and decipherment of the message on page 116:

$$\begin{pmatrix} 7 & 9 \\ 3 & 12 \end{pmatrix} \cdot \begin{pmatrix} 18 & 19 \\ 15 & 17 \end{pmatrix} = \begin{pmatrix} 126 + 135 & 133 + 153 \\ 54 + 180 & 57 + 204 \end{pmatrix} = \begin{pmatrix} 261 & 286 \\ 234 & 261 \end{pmatrix}$$

$$\equiv \begin{pmatrix} 1 & 0 \\ 0 & 1 \end{pmatrix} \quad (\text{mod } 26).$$

The above multiplication shows how to verify that one matrix is the inverse of another.

We present now a method of calculating the inverse of a matrix. It requires the use of a concept known as a *determinant* and defined as follows: Given a 2 × 2 matrix

$$M = \begin{pmatrix} m_{11} & m_{12} \\ m_{21} & m_{22} \end{pmatrix},$$

its determinant, written

$$|M| = \begin{vmatrix} m_{11} & m_{12} \\ m_{21} & m_{22} \end{vmatrix}$$

with straight lines instead of curved lines, is the *number*

$$d = m_{11}m_{22} - m_{12}m_{21}.$$

Note that different matrices may have the same determinant.

Examples:

$$\begin{vmatrix} 1 & 2 \\ 2 & 6 \end{vmatrix} = (1)(6) - (2)(2) = 2,$$

$$\begin{vmatrix} 8 & 3 \\ 2 & 1 \end{vmatrix} = (8)(1) - (3)(2) = 2,$$

$$\begin{vmatrix} 14 & 3 \\ 4 & 1 \end{vmatrix} = (14)(1) - (3)(4) = 2.$$

We shall now prove that *the inverse of M*, which we denote by M^{-1} is

(4.3) $$M^{-1} = \begin{pmatrix} \dfrac{m_{22}}{d} & \dfrac{-m_{12}}{d} \\[2ex] \dfrac{-m_{21}}{d} & \dfrac{m_{11}}{d} \end{pmatrix}.$$

Of course, if numbers like m_{ij}/d are to exist in our modular arithmetic it is necessary for d to be an odd number not divisible by 13.

Conversely, if d satisfies that requirement, all the elements in M^{-1} can be calculated.

The proof consists in multiplying M by M^{-1} and showing that the result is I.

$$
\begin{pmatrix} m_{11} & m_{12} \\ \\ m_{21} & m_{22} \end{pmatrix} \cdot \begin{pmatrix} \dfrac{m_{22}}{d} & \dfrac{-m_{12}}{d} \\ \\ \dfrac{-m_{21}}{d} & \dfrac{m_{11}}{d} \end{pmatrix}
$$

$$
= \begin{pmatrix} \dfrac{m_{11}m_{22} - m_{12}m_{21}}{d} & \dfrac{-m_{11}m_{12} + m_{11}m_{12}}{d} \\ \\ \dfrac{m_{21}m_{22} - m_{21}m_{22}}{d} & \dfrac{m_{11}m_{22} - m_{12}m_{21}}{d} \end{pmatrix} .
$$

Since $d = m_{11}m_{22} - m_{12}m_{21}$, this reduces to

$$
\begin{pmatrix} 1 & 0 \\ 0 & 1 \end{pmatrix} = I.
$$

The reader can easily check that also $M^{-1} \cdot M = I$, thus verifying our earlier assertion that the product of a matrix by its inverse in either order is I.

The above calculation shows that a necessary and sufficient condition for a 2×2 matrix to have an inverse is that its determinant be an odd number not divisible by 13. Making use of this fact, we can easily pick keys for encipherment. If the matrix selected for the transformation has a determinant satisfying the condition just obtained—d is prime to 26—a deciphering matrix exists and can be calculated.

The restrictions on d arise from the fact that 26 is divisible by 2 and 13. If our alphabet had happened to have a prime number p of letters in it, any integer not divisible by p would be acceptable as the value of the determinant. This has given rise to the development of some cryptographic systems in which the number of letters involved is deliberately made prime. For example, if we eliminate three letters from our alphabet by writing C for both itself and K, I for itself and J, U for itself and V, there would then be only 23 letters, and every matrix whose determinant is not zero (mod 23) would have an inverse. Similarly if we increase our alphabet to 29 characters by adding three, like *period, comma* and *question mark*, we get a corresponding result, viz. any matrix whose determinant is not a multiple of the prime 29 has an inverse. These variations of procedure are of special interest, but will not be considered any further.

A property of determinants whose verification we leave to the student as an exercise is the following: If the matrices M, N, P are such that $M \cdot N = P$, then

$$|M| \cdot |N| = |P|.$$

In words, *the determinant of a product matrix is the product of the determinants.*

Exercises

64. Multiply (modulo 26)

   (a) $M = \begin{pmatrix} 2 & 5 \\ 7 & 8 \end{pmatrix}$ by $N = \begin{pmatrix} 4 & 1 \\ 3 & 2 \end{pmatrix}$;

   (b) $A = \begin{pmatrix} 5 & 2 \\ 6 & 7 \end{pmatrix}$ by itself.

65. Calculate the determinant of

   (a) $\begin{pmatrix} 1 & 6 \\ 3 & 23 \end{pmatrix}$ (b) $\begin{pmatrix} 2 & 3 \\ 3 & 5 \end{pmatrix}$ (c) $\begin{pmatrix} 20 & 2 \\ 5 & 4 \end{pmatrix}$ (d) $\begin{pmatrix} 5 & 4 \\ 4 & 5 \end{pmatrix}$

66. Determine the inverse (modulo 26) of

   (a) $\begin{pmatrix} 5 & 2 \\ 7 & 3 \end{pmatrix}$ (b) $\begin{pmatrix} 2 & 3 \\ 1 & 22 \end{pmatrix}$ (c) $\begin{pmatrix} 4 & 11 \\ 1 & 22 \end{pmatrix}$

67. (a) If the determinant of a matrix is 9, what is the determinant of its inverse (mod 26)?

   (b) If the determinant of a matrix is 10, what is the determinant of its inverse:

   (i) mod 26?   (ii) mod 23?   (iii) mod 29?

4.3 Involutory transformations

Some simplifications in the handling of a digraphic system based on a linear transformation would be obtained if we designed the system so that the enciphering matrix is its own inverse. This is the same as saying that the matrix M used to encipher a message can also be used for decipherment. M followed by M is the identity. In terms of the product property this means that

$$M \cdot M \equiv I, \quad \text{or} \quad M^2 \equiv I; \quad \text{also } M \equiv M^{-1}.$$

The *period* of a matrix is defined as the smallest positive power of that matrix which is the identity (if such a power exists). If $M^2 = I$, but $M \neq I$, M is of period 2. A matrix of period 2 is called *involutory*. Since the determinant of the identity matrix is

$$|I| = \begin{vmatrix} 1 & 0 \\ 0 & 1 \end{vmatrix} = 1(1) - 0(0) = 1,$$

the determinant of an involutory matrix must be a number whose square is 1. It is therefore congruent either to 1 or to 25 (mod 26). This is a necessary condition, but it is not sufficient; it is possible for a matrix to have determinant congruent to 1 or 25 and not be involutory.

Examples:

$$M = \begin{pmatrix} 2 & 3 \\ 25 & 24 \end{pmatrix}$$

is an involutory matrix. Its determinant is congruent to 25 and it is its own inverse: $M^2 \equiv I$.

$N = \begin{pmatrix} 1 & 2 \\ 2 & 5 \end{pmatrix}$ has determinant 1, but its square is $\begin{pmatrix} 5 & 12 \\ 12 & 3 \end{pmatrix}$.

N is not involutory.

There are only 7 instances of involutory matrices with determinant 1, and these are of limited cryptographic interest. We suggest as an exercise that the reader determine these matrices and the specialized digraphic substitutions they generate. (Hint: Show first that if $d = 1$ and $M = M^{-1}$, then $m_{11} \equiv m_{22}$ and $2m_{12} \equiv 2m_{21} \equiv 0$.)

If the determinant of a matrix M is congruent to -1 (i.e. to 25), then M is involutory if and only if $m_{11} + m_{22} \equiv 0$ (i.e. congruent to 26). The proof is as follows:

Given

$$M = \begin{pmatrix} m_{11} & m_{12} \\ m_{21} & m_{22} \end{pmatrix} \quad \text{with} \quad d \equiv -1;$$

its inverse M^{-1} is

$$\begin{pmatrix} \dfrac{m_{22}}{d} & \dfrac{-m_{12}}{d} \\ \dfrac{-m_{21}}{d} & \dfrac{m_{11}}{d} \end{pmatrix}.$$

Since $d \equiv -1$,

$$M^{-1} \equiv \begin{pmatrix} -m_{22} & m_{12} \\ m_{21} & -m_{11} \end{pmatrix}.$$

Therefore

$$M^{-1} \equiv \begin{pmatrix} m_{11} & m_{12} \\ m_{21} & m_{22} \end{pmatrix} = M$$

if and only if $-m_{22} \equiv m_{11}$ and $-m_{11} \equiv m_{22}$, that is, if and only if

$$m_{11} + m_{22} \equiv 0.$$

Since in that case M is its own inverse, it is involutory.

With the knowledge that $d \equiv -1$ and $m_{11} + m_{22} \equiv 0$, it is relatively simple to construct involutory matrices.

Example: Choose $m_{11} = 2$. Then $m_{22} = 24$, and

$$d \equiv 48 - m_{12}m_{21} \equiv 25,$$

so that $m_{12}m_{21} \equiv 23$. Any two numbers whose product is $\equiv 23$ can be chosen as m_{12} and m_{21}. They can be 23, 1 or 7, 7 or 3, 25 or 15, 5 etc.

Exercises

68. Determine the period, i.e. the number n such that $M^n \equiv I \pmod{26}$, of

(a) $\begin{pmatrix} 3 & 0 \\ 0 & 1 \end{pmatrix}$;   (b) $\begin{pmatrix} 3 & 4 \\ 4 & 23 \end{pmatrix}$.

69. Determine the value of a which will make the following matrices involutory:

(a) $\begin{pmatrix} 2 & 7 \\ 7 & a \end{pmatrix}$,   (b) $\begin{pmatrix} 3 & 4 \\ a & 23 \end{pmatrix}$,   (c) $\begin{pmatrix} 5 & a \\ 10 & 21 \end{pmatrix}$.

70. Suppose an involutory transformation enciphers the plain digraph DE as CI. How would it encipher the word DECIDE?

4.4 Recognition of digraphic ciphers

We place ourselves now in the cryptanalyst's role and examine the problem of how we would attempt to solve a message enciphered digraphically, by a linear transformation. Here is the problem.

```
IXXZK YRVGP JTCMM GIYGE YQMXZ DANSG HERUQ JCZBQ
ZQXAP CQCSG RUIPB CDAXZ ANMIO DTFIB AJKLS GASMX
SYWGO UQUFF CPSGA YCMMC SXKMR INAXA FNESE FHTYS
IJGEQ AHEYN LQOQD CIQXZ QAXZE ZQCOD FACVY QGTES
YXYSZ SOZWA CKLAR SESBL YQLQX ALAZW UOGLJ YYYXZ
ANQPK PWNVU EMIVF OCKBC BMLED IAEHE ZSSGY QEMXZ
UJSRC BHUSG QWMKZ WCKZQ RFSOY QGLZI SLTOP PQAEJ
DNZQZ WGYGW UDHJT EWNDA VGBGZ QZWQJ JUPXB CDAMX
XZQAX ZANKQ KNTSZ QXAZQ ZBHEW HHTQA XZEUO HHESG
TOXAX VUBBR QPXVG WHEMQ OUWGS GQAAN TCVPM NQNUW
FMXKW HXJEF WHCMS GXZAN KQKNT SILRI UAUEC MMJTS
YRRRQ CTAXQ TOKY
```

The cryptanalyst's first task is to get some idea of the cryptographic system which was used for encipherment. This begins with a trigraphic frequency table and a search for repetitions in the cipher.

From the frequency distribution, which will not be reproduced, it is clear that the message could not possibly be a monoalphabet. The monographic distribution is relatively flat, and the index of coincidence is .041.

What about the possibility of a polyalphabet? There are many repetitions. We list below, in order of size, all repetitions of at least four letters

Repetitions	Locations of first letter		Interval	Factors
XZANKQKNTS	325	417	92	2,2,23
XZQAXZ	139	321	182	2,7,13
ZQXA	41	335	294	2,3,7,7
BCDA	55	315	260	2,2,5,13
AXZE	142	350	208	2,2,2,2,13
XZAN	199	325	126	2,3,3,7
ZQZW	283	305	22	2,11
QAXZ	323	349	26	2,13

It is extremely unlikely that either the ten-letter repetition or the six-letter repetition could be accidental. The only common factor their intervals have is 2. Since 2 is a factor of every repetition interval, we check the possibility that the message involves 2 alphabets. The indices of coincidence are found to be .042 and .045, numbers which are unacceptably small.

Since the message is not polyalphabetic and yet has 2 as a factor of every one of the repetition intervals, the next question must be: Is the system digraphic? To answer that question we construct a digraphic frequency table. We divide the message into digraphs and prepare a tally of individual digraphs. The tally is shown in Figure 19.

Suppose the digraphic system is one in which a plain text digraph, whenever it occurs, is always replaced by the same cipher digraph. Then, in one sense, we could consider the system to be monoalphabetic on an alphabet of $26 \times 26 = 676$ characters. Each of these characters (digraphs) has a characteristic frequency in plain language. The reasoning which we developed in Chapter 3 on the index of coincidence is applicable. If we calculate the sum of the squares of the characteristic frequencies of the 676 digraphs, we get the number .0069, which we can use as a measure of roughness of a (monoalphabetic) digraphic system. For a flat digraphic distribution, M.R. is $1/676 \approx .0015$.

The index of coincidence derivable from our digraphic frequency table is calculated as

$$\frac{\sum_{i=\mathrm{AA}}^{i=\mathrm{ZZ}} f_i(f_i - 1)}{N(N-1)} \, ,$$

where N is the number of digraphs, i.e. half the length of the message, and the f_i are the frequencies of the cipher digraphs. Carrying out the calculation, we get .0084. We can consider then that it has been established that the underlying system is digraphic, and that repeated occurrences of any cipher digraph will always have the same plain text equivalent. We have no evidence, though, as yet, of what kind of digraphic system it is.

4.5   Solution of a linear transformation

There are many different kinds of digraphic systems. The linear transformation we have been studying is just one of these systems. If we have any reason for suspecting that a linear transformation has been used, we can keep that fact in mind and can make special tests in accordance with that idea. Thus if we could identify two or more plain-cipher equivalents, we could set up congruences with the matrix elements serving as the unknowns. Two plain-cipher equivalents would yield four congruences which might be sufficient to determine all four unknowns. If there are ambiguities resulting from the solutions of these congruences, they can be separately tried against additional text to determine the correct choices. If more than two digraphs can be identified, the additional congruences will probably ensure uniqueness of results. These would then decipher the message and produce plain text. Of course, we are assuming that we know the letter-number correspondence that the cryptographers are using.

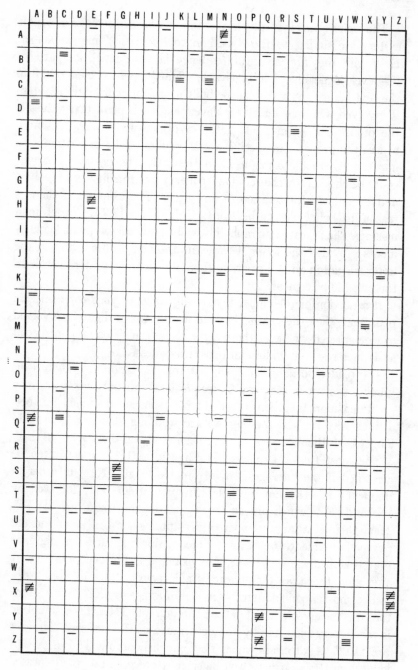

Figure 19

The techniques for getting a start toward the solution of a digraphic system are similar to those used in coping with a monoalphabet. Essentially they are the use of frequency data and repetition patterns for developing some plain text values. These have to be entered into the text before any ideas can be built up as to what kind of system is involved. One possibility for developing such plain text values is the probable word method. If the cryptanalyst has any reason to expect the presence of specific words or phrases, he can attempt to find out where these might fit in the text. The possible positions could be checked by the relative frequencies of the digraphs involved and by pattern information, if any exists. For example, if there is reason to believe that the words UNITED STATES occur in a message, the repeated digraph TE will be a check on possible placements provided the letter U falls in an even position. Should the letter U fall in an odd position, there would be no pattern check on the possible placement.

If a portion of the cipher text is suspected to yield some specific plain text, then the values obtained for the cipher digraphs involved can be entered wherever those digraphs appear. This may in special situations result in additional text being guessed.

The reader no doubt realizes that the derivation of text in a digraphic system by the use of frequencies and patterns requires a great deal more text than is needed for the solution of a monoalphabet. This is why the test message we are studying now is substantially longer than the messages we have been studying thus far.

The most frequent digraph in English is TH. It can often be identified if the message is of reasonable length. Next in order of frequency is HE, not much less frequent than TH, followed by IN and ER which are about two thirds the frequency of TH. Then there is a large number of digraphs which can be considered relatively frequent. On the low frequency side there are some digraphs that practically never occur. For example Q is never followed by anything other than U in normal English text.

The most frequent digraph in our message is XZ. We assume that it is the encipherment of the plain digraph TH. This assumption is made very plausible by the occurrence of the repeated sequence XZQAXZ, a pattern in which TH frequently occurs. Thus if XZQA is one word (and it may well be since it precedes the long repeated sequence XZANKQKNTS), the cipher XZQAXZ might be

THAT THE or THAN THE or THEN THE. If XZQA is not a whole word then XZQAXZ might be some combination like OTHER THAN or RATHER THEN. In any case, the correspondence cipher XZ → plain TH looks like a good possibility.

The identification of TH permits a further utilization of frequency information. We have already noted the very high frequency of THE (page 49). Of the 2161 occurrences of TH, 1717 are followed by E. On the average, about four out of five occurrences of TH are followed by E. Suppose we assume that every occurrence of TH in our digraphic problem is followed by E. Then although some of these assumptions may be wrong, the great majority of them will be right. What help can we get from this assumption?

Let us write all the digraphs following the cipher pair XZ. They are

$$\text{KY, AN, QA, EZ, UJ, EU}$$

There are only six different digraphs because XZAN occurs four times, and XZQA occurs twice.

What help can these give us? Let us assume that the system is based on a linear transformation. Then, for each of these cipher digraphs we can write a congruence expressing the fact that the first letter of the plain text digraph which it represents is E. We would thus have six congruences in only two unknowns, of the form

$$b_{11}C_1 + b_{12}C_2 \equiv 5,$$

where b_{11} and b_{12} are the unknowns. We suspect that most of these congruences are valid. If we can prove that three or more of them are consistent, i.e. they all have a common solution for the two unknowns b_{11}, b_{12}, then we would have an indication that the system is one of linear transformation.

To prove such a fact, we would solve two of the congruences and check to see whether the solutions satisfy any of the other congruences. Of course, the two we solve must both correspond to cases in which the first letter of the plain text equivalent is really E. It might therefore require more than one attempt at picking a pair of congruences to start with, because some of the digraphs may represent a plain text equivalent whose first letter is not E.

A similar, but quicker, approach would take advantage of the fact that the right member of every one of the congruences is the same number, the equivalent of E. The subtraction of one congruence from a second would thus yield a homogeneous congruence, that is, one of the form $qb_{11} + rb_{12} \equiv 0$.

Let us examine the numerical equivalents of the letters involved in the six digraphs:

$$KY \rightarrow 11, 25$$
$$AN \rightarrow 1, 14$$
$$QA \rightarrow 17, 1$$
$$EZ \rightarrow 5, 26$$
$$UJ \rightarrow 21, 10$$
$$EU \rightarrow 5, 21$$

We note an interesting property. If we choose the digraphs AN, KY, UJ, EU, in that order, we find that the common difference (mod 26) between the numerical equivalents 1, 11, 21, 5 of their first members is 10, and the common difference between those of their second members is 11. This indicates that congruences for those four digraphs are consistent because if we write them out,

$$1b_{11} + 14b_{12} \equiv 5$$
$$11b_{11} + 25b_{12} \equiv 5$$
$$21b_{11} + 10b_{12} \equiv 5$$
$$5b_{11} + 21b_{12} \equiv 5,$$

and then subtract any one of these congruences from the one below it, we get $10b_{11} + 11b_{12} \equiv 0$. Each of these pairs would consequently have the same solution for b_{11} and b_{12}. Since AN occurs four times, this means that seven of the ten times the plain digraph TH is followed by E.

If we solve two of these congruences, we get

$$b_{11} = 3, \qquad b_{12} = 2,$$

and these values satisfy the other two congruences.

These values do not satisfy the congruences formed by assuming that the first letter of the plain text equivalents of QA and EZ is E. This means that the plain text equivalents of QA and EZ begin with some letter other than E. It would be interesting to check the decipherments of their first letters to see what they do give. We may do this by means of the now known values of b_{11} and b_{12}:

$$\text{QA yields: } 17(3) + 1(2) \equiv 53 \equiv 1 \to A$$
$$\text{EZ yields: } 5(3) + 26(2) \equiv 15 \to O$$

Both these letters form good trigraphs with TH. In particular, A_p confirms the possibility that the repetition XZQAXZ represents THAT THE or THAN THE.

We have one other equivalent we have not yet utilized. We know that XZ $\to$ TH. Substituting 3 for b_{11} and 2 for b_{12}, we obtain the value

$$24(3) + 26(2) \equiv 20$$

which is, indeed, the numerical equivalent of T. That's good.

We can use the second letter of this equivalence to get some information about the remaining elements, b_{21}, b_{22}, of our deciphering matrix. We substitute into $C_1 b_{21} + C_2 b_{22} \equiv P_2$ and obtain

$$24 b_{21} + 26 b_{22} \equiv 8.$$

This reduces to

$$24 b_{21} \equiv 8,$$

and has the two solutions

$$b_{21} = 9 \quad \text{or} \quad b_{22} = 22.$$

This information will not be utilized immediately, but will be held in reserve.

The two known elements b_{11}, b_{12} of the deciphering matrix determine the first of the two deciphering congruences, which enables us, for each cipher digraph, to calculate the first letter of its plain text equivalent. We can thus determine all the letters of the original plain text which are in odd numbered positions. The decipherments of these letters for the first ten groups are shown below:

```
IXXZK YRVGP JTCMM GIYGE YQMXZ DANSG HERUQ JCZBQ ZQXAP CQCSG
w the   t a   r i a   y e   e i h   e s   h r s   i n   h v b   e s
```

It is an interesting exercise for the reader to see how well he can fill in the text of a message for which only the odd letters are known. He will undoubtedly discover that it is not as easy as it may seem at first thought.

We don't have to do this, though. All we need to do is to determine the equivalents of some additional digraphs, and we shall be able to solve for the missing members b_{21}, b_{22} of the transformation matrix. To this end we seek a likely place to guess text. A good possibility appears in groups 9 and 10 where we have

$$\text{ZQXAP CQCSG}$$
$$\text{h.v.b .e.s.}$$

The text looks like HAVE BEEN.

From our frequency chart we see that the digraph ZQ, for which the plain equivalent looks like HA, occurs six times in the message. Two of these occurrences are in the repetition ZQXA. When we hunt up the occurrence of ZQXA in groups 67, 68 we find the pattern

$$\text{ZQXAZQZB}$$

We have possible equivalents for ZQ and XA, and we can calculate the first letter of the decipherment of ZB. The resulting text is HAVE HAD. This makes a very good check. We can therefore accept the words HAVE BEEN as correct and write

$$\text{ZQ} \rightarrow \text{HA}$$
$$\text{XA} \rightarrow \text{VE}$$
$$\text{PC} \rightarrow \text{BE}$$
$$\text{QC} \rightarrow \text{EN}$$

With these values we can now determine the two unknown elements b_{21}, b_{22} in the deciphering transformation, i.e. those which correspond to the second congruence.

From ZQ $\rightarrow$ HA, we get

$$26b_{21} + 17b_{22} \equiv 1$$
$$17b_{22} \equiv 1$$
$$b_{22} = 23.$$

To solve for b_{21} it will be easiest to go to the congruence resulting from $QC \rightarrow EN$, viz.

$$17b_{21} + 3b_{22} \equiv 14,$$

because the coefficient of the unknown quantity b_{21} is prime to 26 and will yield only one solution:

$$17b_{21} + 3(23) \equiv 14,$$
$$17b_{21} \equiv 23,$$
$$b_{21} = 9.$$

This value for b_{21} is checked by the information we had already determined (page 137) by using $XZ \rightarrow TH$.

We have then the complete deciphering transformation

$$\begin{pmatrix} 3 & 2 \\ 9 & 23 \end{pmatrix}$$

and can decipher the entire message. The text begins:
WITH EXTRAORDINARY FEVERISHNESS.

Exercises

71. When suspected text has a recognizable pattern it can provide a means of entry into a message. The following message contains the name GEORGE PAPANDREOU.

CMYPZ GTAYO EQBYQ JLAOW INELN NECNN UESZT YTFRU OWYXH
KYADM NJRUK CUFZP YPNNM XWSQQ OJMGO JZQZQ FLVAY XGIPR
OPUFJ WTSVA ATQU

72. There is reason to suspect that the following message relates to the use of computers by the Defense Department to select employees for promotion.

TWQZK XKBSD TWPOE QIAPS XMTSF HQNKB NOIAH NEPOW FYKGQ
ZVGKK OVKBG WYDYI IRYOH GNUHN UVAHY DRYQE KWDNB QBZHN
DAOVK BGWYD OOIIQ ANUYI IRYOH GTTLG GHQED NNKYD OZNUF
JOWYV TWARV YARFW NGSMY IAUCQ QEYII KARQN SSXEI NCCOM
SDJHN GIJDK YGCRT QEQUE ZGJUH EAQWK UFLBL QDVGE UVHNO
WLEWA YRHNU VAHYD RYQEK WDNBQ BZSBV GHRTQ NEKMF AXMZG
GUZOK XVKFK PJLGN QKOSA MPIAH EWPMW UYIGI KSBLO LZOWF
YKGQZ WV

73. BPCNT QZVNS CWVWZ GBPRI IBYLA CULBP DEZSB PECLE UKGXQ
    AGPCW FKIZX GOZCZ KWUUN TRWBP MBGHD IKGPH BEPDQ AGPPM
    SUZPX WDSIU GQYTG MKJDS JOKOG MKGGX UHPMK MXAPH LSBIG
    RQFOQ IZYLB QSUAG TMNYT GTUJO YSLSA YBUYL VVUUT GBPAT
    IZYXC ZKWUU NTXJF QBPHY TQNVR IOPKK EIAGP MSUZP ALZSK
    APIQK NNULB PBWGM GCONM BAOAG WBNMZ MONBP DEXGB PNSWB
    ACYLJ ZQAKM ESNIZ PBPXG MSZPY LBQUL BPTQB QYLGM RVDEK
    MRJQM KTBQB PRIAS TEULM WKWRG CDPMS UZPUH IBQDX GYQOQ
    ULNMZ MGZGR MWKWW BBPAT CHYXQ QNNNG DEYLF JSNXG LBBAN
    PPOEH XOONB QTXKV BIIUL OWFFM ONDBO ECRUU SUKMO NYNOV

4.6   How to make the Hill System more secure

Suppose now that the cryptographer has become aware of how a message, enciphered by a linear transformation system, was deciphered. He wishes to strengthen the system by modifications aimed at the weaknesses that the cryptanalyst was able to attack.

It would seem fairly evident that he would direct his attention first to the fact that the letter-number correspondence was available to the cryptanalyst. With the use of that correspondence, the cryptanalyst was able to set up the equations which permitted him to determine the elements of the transformation matrix. Why not make the letter-number correspondence part of the specific key?

For example, an agreed keyword could be used to set up a mixed sequence. Then the letters of that sequence could be numbered 1 to 26, thus providing a scrambled, unknown letter-number correspondence. Now, even if the cryptanalyst is aware that the system is one of linear transformation, he needs to determine 30 unknown quantities—the four elements of the matrix and the 26 numerical equivalents of the letters of the alphabet. To accomplish such a result would require the correct identification of a large number of cipher digraphs and would undoubtedly demand a greatly increased amount of cipher text.

To add a further aspect of security, it is possible to use one letter-number correspondence in going from plain letters to numbers in encipherment and a second letter-number correspondence to replace the calculated numbers by cipher letters. Such a step adds twenty-six more unknowns.

With these changes we seem to be developing an interesting cryptographic system. It still remains true that there is information derivable from digraphic frequencies and patterns, provided a sufficient amount of material is available. To eliminate that capability, we could use a trigraphic instead of a digraphic system. That is, we could use three congruences in three unknowns

$$C_1 \equiv a_{11}P_1 + a_{12}P_2 + a_{13}P_3$$
$$C_2 \equiv a_{21}P_1 + a_{22}P_2 + a_{23}P_3$$
$$C_3 \equiv a_{31}P_1 + a_{32}P_2 + a_{33}P_3.$$

Having picked a matrix which has an inverse, the cryptographic system would replace the plain text three letters at a time by cipher combinations.

And, of course, one need not stop at three. The system could be tetragraphic or pentagraphic affording increasing security with each increase in the size of the unit.

The limitations are practical ones. The necessary amount of computation increases very greatly with increasing sizes of transformation matrices. In addition, the chances of error become much greater. Since any single error affects all the letters of the group being enciphered, the use of a large size unit introduces increasing risk that a few errors in enciphering or in transmission may garble a large portion of the text. In such cases the recipient may not be able to read the message he has received. This is a major consideration against the use of large matrices.

CHAPTER FIVE

Transposition

5.1 Columnar transposition

A type of encipherment procedure quite different in character from the substitution ciphers we have been describing is called *transposition*. Such a system does not change the identities of the letters of the message; it rearranges their positions.

Here are some simple examples of transpositions used to encipher the message

I CAME I SAW I CONQUERED

a. The text could be written backwards.

DEREU QNOCI WASIE MACI

b. The Rail Fence Cipher. The text is written with alternate letters on each of two rows, and then read row by row.

```
I   A   E   S   W   C   N   U   R   D
  C   M   I   A   I   O   Q   E   E
```
Cipher: IAESW CNURD CMIAI OQEE

c. The system could select a geometric figure and inscribe the message in it according to one route or direction of writing, and then transcribe the message according to a second route, as for example in Figure 20.

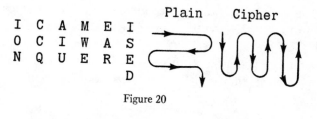

```
I  C  A  M  E  I
O  C  I  W  A  S
N  Q  U  E  R  E
            D
```

Figure 20

Cipher: IONQC CAIUE WMEAR DESI

The effect of any transposition cipher is to rearrange the letters of the original message. This effect can be represented mathematically by means of a concept called a *permutation*. To illustrate it, consider the backwards writing Example a. in the preceding paragraph. The message has 19 letters. Designate them by the numbers representing their positions in the plain text message so that the plain text message consists of the numbers 1 to 19. Applying the enciphering procedure to the plain text produces the cipher message

19 18 17 16 15 14 13 12 11 10 9 8 7 6 5 4 3 2 1

Write the cipher under the plain text,

Plain   1 2 3 4 5 6 7 8 9 10 11 12 13 14 15 16 17 18 19
Cipher 19 18 17 16 15 14 13 12 11 10 9 8 7 6 5 4 3 2 1

In this representation the permutation shows the position each letter occupies in the original message (on the upper line) and its final position in the cipher message (on the lower line).

A permutation is a kind of rule by means of which the elements of a set are replaced, in a one-to-one fashion, by members of the same set. More precisely: it is a one-to-one function or mapping of a set onto itself. The permutation in Example a. may be expressed by means of the function

$$f: \quad k \rightarrow 20 - k, \qquad k = 1, 2, \cdots, 19.$$

The notation can be simplified to a one-line representation, by means of a chaining process similar to that used in reconstructing Vigenère sequences (p. 105). Starting with the number 1, we follow it by the number below it in the cipher line: 19. Then, since 19 in the plain line has a 1 below it, we follow 19 by 1. But that completes a cycle. So we write the pair of numbers (1, 19) in parentheses to signify that 1 goes to 19 and 19 goes to 1. Then we start a chain with the number 2 and get (2, 18). Continuing in this way, we find the complete permutation to consist of cycles of two numbers each except for the number 10 which is replaced by itself and forms a cycle of just one number:

$$(1,19) \ (2,18) \ (3,17) \ (4,16) \ (5,15) \ (6,14) \ (7,13) \ (8,12) \ (9,11) \ (10)$$

We will agree to omit the writing of any such number as the 10 above, which is in a cycle by itself.

If we apply this same procedure to the Rail Fence Cipher (Example b.), we get the cipher message

M: 1   3   5   7   9 11 13 15 17 19   2   4   6   8 10 12 14 16 18

Writing this under the plain text message we have

```
1 2 3 4 5   6   7   8   9 10 11 12 13 14 15 16 17 18 19
1 3 5 7 9  11  13  15  17 19  2  4  6  8 10 12 14 16 18
```

Now apply the chaining procedure. We end up with one cycle of 18 numbers

N: (2, 3, 5, 9, 17, 14, 8, 15, 10, 19, 18, 16, 12, 4, 7, 13, 6, 11)

In most cases of transposition ciphers, the resulting permutation consists of several cycles with no particular relation between their lengths. The total number of letters represented in these cycles is less than the length of the message by the number of letters whose positions are unchanged, i.e. are in cycles consisting of just one number.

The advantages of using the permutation concept for transposition are mainly theoretical. As the reader can quickly determine by taking two examples of different lengths and transposing them by the same type of transposition system, the resulting permutations usually look quite different. This means that the permutation which expresses the result of a transposition is a function not only of the method but also of the length of the message. Consequently the permutation procedure is not really practical for enciphering and deciphering messages of differing lengths.

One question which the permutation notation helps answer readily is: What happens if a transposition procedure is applied repeatedly? To examine this, let us take the Rail Fence Cipher as an illustration and apply it twice. Thus, we take the cipher message M on page 144 and put it through a Rail Fence transposition.

$$
\begin{array}{ccccccccc}
1 & 5 & 9 & 13 & 17 & 2 & 6 & 10 & 14 & 18 \\
 & 3 & 7 & 11 & 15 & 19 & 4 & 8 & 12 & 16
\end{array}
$$

We write the resulting cipher under the original message:

$$
\begin{array}{ccccccccccccccccccc}
1 & 2 & 3 & 4 & 5 & 6 & 7 & 8 & 9 & 10 & 11 & 12 & 13 & 14 & 15 & 16 & 17 & 18 & 19 \\
1 & 5 & 9 & 13 & 17 & 2 & 6 & 10 & 14 & 18 & 3 & 7 & 11 & 15 & 19 & 4 & 8 & 12 & 16
\end{array}
$$

The permutation which corresponds to this transposition of the original text is

$$(2,5,17,8,10,18,12,7,6)(3,9,14,15,19,16,4,13,11).$$

On comparing it with the permutation resulting from a single application of the Rail Fence Cipher (N on page 144), we see that the permutation we have after the second step is a decimation at interval 2 of the first result. And, in general, it can be shown that n applications of the transposition yield a decimation at interval n of the original permutation.

This result now permits us to answer the question: How many times does a transposition have to be applied before the cipher becomes identical with the original plain text? Consider a single cycle of the original permutation, say of length x. Such a cycle is reduced to cycles of one letter only if decimated at any interval which is a multiple of x. In other words, all the letters of that cycle return to their original positions if the transposition is repeated a multiple of x times. Since such a statement is true for every cycle, *the number of times a transposition must be applied to return to the original plain language message is the least common multiple of the lengths of all the cycles included in it.* As a simple illustration, the backwards writing cipher (Example a.) becomes plain text if applied twice since all its cycles are of length two.

Suppose the permutation which expresses the result of the transposition process consists of the cycles

$$(1,14,9) \quad (10,15,2,6) \quad (5,16,3,11,4) \quad (12,7,18,13,8,17).$$

Then the number of applications required to reduce the cipher to plain text is the least common multiple of 3, 4, 5 and 6 which is 60.

A common transposition procedure is one in which the plain text message is inscribed normally into a rectangle with a prearranged number of columns and then transcribed vertically by columns to yield the cipher text. We have already seen one form of this technique in the columnar transposing of keyword mixed sequences (page 39). There, the transcription process was to read the columns in order from left to right. If, however, the columns are read in an irregular order, the system becomes more flexible and gives greater security.

Such a system is called *columnar transposition.* The key is a prearranged sequence of numbers which determines both the width of the inscription rectangle and the order in which the columns are to be transcribed.

To assist in recalling the numerical sequence, it is usually arranged to derive it from an agreed keyword, by assigning numbers to the individual letters of the keyword according to their alphabetical order. The method by which this is done is described in the following example: Suppose the keyword is SORCERY. Then since C is alphabetically the earliest letter in the word, it is numbered 1. E is numbered 2, O is numbered 3. The two R's are numbered 4 and 5, from left to right, after which S and Y are made 6 and 7, respectively. The resulting numerical key is

$$\begin{matrix} S & O & R & C & E & R & Y \\ 6 & 3 & 4 & 1 & 2 & 5 & 7 \end{matrix}$$

We wish to encipher the message

LASER BEAMS CAN BE MODULATED TO CARRY MORE INTELLIGENCE THAN RADIO WAVES

The message is written out on a width of 7, under the numerical sequence:

```
S  O  R  C  E  R  Y
6  3  4  1  2  5  7

L  A  S  E  R  B  E
A  M  S  C  A  N  B
E  M  O  D  U  L  A
T  E  D  T  O  C  A
R  R  Y  M  O  R  E
I  N  T  E  L  L  I
G  E  N  C  E  T  H
A  N  R  A  D  I  O
W  A  V  E  S
```

Since the length of the message is not a multiple of 7, the inscription does not fill the last row of the rectangle. As we shall see shortly, the decipherment process is simplified if the last row contains no blank cells. We shall therefore agree for the general system now being described that the rectangle must always be *completely filled*. If the plain text message is not the right length to complete the last row, null letters must be added to bring this about. Since there are two blank spaces on the last row, we complete the diagram by adding two dummy letters, say Q and R.

```
S  O  R  C  E  R  Y
6  3  4  1  2  5  7

L  A  S  E  R  B  E
A  M  S  C  A  N  B
E  M  O  D  U  L  A
T  E  D  T  O  C  A
R  R  Y  M  O  R  E
I  N  T  E  L  L  I
G  E  N  C  E  T  H
A  N  R  A  D  I  O
W  A  V  E  S  Q  R
```

Now the enciphering process consists of reading out the cipher text vertically in the order of the numbered columns. At the same time it can be written in groups of five letters.

ECDTM ECAER AUOOL EDSAM MERNE NASSO DYTNR VBNLC
RLTIQ LAETR IGAWE BAAEI HOR

The decipherer proceeds as follows: He counts the number of letters
in the message (63). Since the length of the key is 7, the dimensions
of the inscription rectangle are 7 × 9. He rules off such a rectangle
and puts the key above it. He then enters the cipher message into
the diagram in the order of the key numbers; the first nine letters go
under the number 1, then the next nine go in column 2, the next nine
in column 3, etc.

6	3	4	1	2	5	7
	A		E	R		
	M		C	A		
	M		D	U		
	E		T	O		
	R		M	O		
	N		E	L		
	E		C	E		
	N		A	D		
	A		E	S		

When the complete message has been entered, the plain text appears
in normal order.

Exercises

74. Decipher the following message with the key based on the word
    ROYALTY:

    TNGTH CYIIL XHEIH PANCA AXHGR OUFOA EMITE LSOIP INDSR
    ROEAR ERANX EEEFT ILMSE AEANS CESON EX

75. Decipher the following message with the key based on the word
    CREAMPUFF:

    HDUCP IEATL EIEUU OENOI XMMCI TATDF DSSHC HSSVS ISTAO
    TRNGO HRSSG OHASF EMBLH FPEEO EE

5.2 Solution of transpositions with completely filled rectangles

We consider now the cryptanalysis of a transposition using a completely filled rectangle. Our illustrative example is

EOEYE GTRNP SECEH HETYH SNGND DDDET OCRAE RAEMH
TECSE USIAR WKDRI RNYAR ANUEY ICNTT CEIET US

There is, of course, no difficulty in recognizing that a cipher is transposition and not substitution. A monographic distribution of the text of a transposition will match the normal distribution without any shift; in other words, it is the normal distribution. This indicates that the identities of the original letters have not been changed, hence their positions must have been rearranged.

We thus determine that the above message is a transposition, and we are going to assume that it is columnar transposition using a completely filled rectangle. (Later in the chapter we shall see how to solve columnar transpositions without assuming that the rectangle is completely filled.)

The width of a completely filled rectangle must be a divisor of the length of the message; since the text has 77 letters, the rectangle must be either 7 or 11 letters wide. (For messages of other lengths, there might be more possibilities to consider, since the length might have more factors. This would then require an increased amount of work, but no difference in the general principle of attack.) The message is written vertically into rectangles of the possible widths; the two results are shown below:

1	2	3	4	5	6	7	8	9	10	11
E	R	H	N	E	R	C	R	N	E	C
O	N	H	G	T	A	S	W	Y	Y	E
E	P	E	N	O	E	E	K	A	I	I
Y	S	T	D	C	M	U	D	R	C	E
E	E	Y	D	R	H	S	R	A	N	T
G	C	H	D	A	T	I	I	N	T	U
T	E	S	D	E	E	A	R	U	T	S

1	2	3	4	5	6	7
E	E	G	A	E	R	C
O	C	N	E	U	N	N
E	E	D	R	S	Y	T
Y	H	D	A	I	A	T
E	H	D	E	A	R	C
G	E	D	M	R	A	E
T	T	E	H	W	N	I
R	Y	T	T	K	U	E
N	H	O	E	D	E	T
P	S	C	C	R	Y	U
S	N	R	S	I	I	S

If it is correct that the inscription rectangle is completely filled, then a solution will be obtained by rearranging the columns, as units, so as to form plain text. The process of restoring a disarranged set of letters into its original positions is called *anagramming*. Our task is to anagram these columns to form plain text.

Since the first row of letters represents the beginning of the message, we might start by trying to reconstruct the first word. Examining the rectangle of width 11, we note that of the first eleven letters only 3 are vowels, a very unlikely distribution of vowels and consonants. Also, the fourth row has only three vowels. It does not seem likely that the correct rectangle is eleven columns wide.

We concentrate then on the width 7. What could the first word be? Perhaps we have some difficulty in anagramming the letters of the first row. Then the next step should be to try to fit two columns together so as to get good digraphs. (An aid in this process is to write the columns on individual slips of paper which can be moved about easily.) We note that column 7 followed by column 2 produces many good digraphs, including, in particular, two occurrences of TH.

```
            7 2

            C E
            N C
            T E
            T H
            C H
            E E
            I T
            E Y
            T H
            U S
            S N
```

The seventh row suggests the possibility of finding an H to follow the T. There is one, in column 4. If we try column 4 next to column 2, we get very good combinations, in particular the word THE and the trigraph THA. The only impossible combination is SNS on the last row. Should this cause us to discard the combinations we have just formed? No. What we have seems too good. There is a possibility that the letters SNS on the last line may be nulls.

```
1 3 5 6    7 2 4

E G E R    C E A
O N U N    N C E
E D S Y    T E R
Y D I A    T H A
E D A R    C H E
G D R A    E E M
T E W N    I T H
R T K U    E Y T
N O D E    T H E
P C R Y    U S C
S R I I    S N S
```

The THA suggests the word THAT. But there is no T available on row 4, nor is there a T available on row 5 to allow for the possibility that column 4 is the rightmost column. It seems hard to say what letter should follow the THA. Proceeding down to row 7, the W looks like a good letter to precede ITH. We place that column in front of the three we already have.

```
1 3 6    5 7 2 4

E G R    E C E A
O N N    U N C E
E D Y    S T E R
Y D A    I T H A
E D R    A C H E
G D A    R E E M
T E N    W I T H
R T U    K E Y T
N O E    D T H E
P C Y    R U S C
S R I    I S N S
```

Now the answer strikes the eye. The eighth line suggests the word TURKEY and the tenth line yields CYPRUS from which we see that the first word is GREECE. The transposition is solved and the key is 3 6 1 5 7 2 4. The last two letters N and S are clearly nulls and should be discarded.

In this general way, it is possible to solve a transposition corresponding to a completely filled rectangle. Anagramming the columns to form plain text is a reasonably straightforward process. There may be a number of different widths to consider, but getting a solution is normally just a matter of time.

Exercises

76. Solve this transposition which involves a completely filled rectangle:

    EOECO HENIO DAART TARTL ODYFS OVNQN AELAF SGNOP TESWP
    NITET IENOI EHIGI RLBIE CSTEC EFDOW ECXTR SRXSU ONCSV
    AIHGE PAA

77. Solve the following transposition (note the various occurrences of the letter X which help determine the length of the keyword):

    NSGVA ENXEH THLSO XNDFP ESNIA OAGDI RXPMR YEALS AECHN
    TAEOU OASMU XMERE NNTXO UYART LXLCP SAECX

5.3 Incompletely filled rectangles

We have seen that if the rectangle is completely filled, the crypt-analyst's task is merely one of anagramming entire columns. The very slight change in the cryptographic system of making the last row shorter than the full width of the rectangle introduces a sub-stantial improvement in security. If necessary, nulls are introduced at the end of the plain text to insure that there are blank cells at the right end of the last row.

Consider first how the enciphering and deciphering procedures are changed by this modification of the system. Let the keyword be PRINCETON and let the message be

THE HOUSE VOTED YESTERDAY TO CUT BACK FOREIGN AID

The inscription diagram is

```
P R I N C E T O N
7 8 3 4 1 2 9 6 5

T H E H O U S E V
O T E D Y E S T E
R D A Y T O C U T
B A C K F O R E I
G N A I D
```

and the cipher message is

OYTFD UEOOE EACAH DYKIV ETIET UETOR BGHTD ANSSC R

In order to decipher this message, it is necessary to determine the inscription diagram. To do this, the decipherer begins with a count of the number of letters in order to determine the lengths of the columns. There are 41 letters and the keyword is 9 letters long. Since 41 divided by 9 gives 4 as a quotient and a remainder of 5, there will be four complete rows and one partial row of 5 letters. Or, in other words, there will be five columns of five letters each and four columns of four letters each. The diagram for decipherment will be

7 8 3 4 1 2 9 6 5

The cipher message is written into the diagram in the order of the key numbers. OYTFD go into column 1, UEOO into column 2, EEACA into column 3, etc. until the entire cipher message has been entered into the transposition figure.

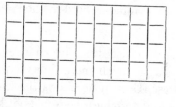

7 8 3 4 1 2 9 6 5

7	8	3	4	1	2	9	6	5
		E		O	U			
		E		Y	E			
		A		T	O			
		C		F	O			
		A		D				

Then the plain text can be read normally.

Exercises

78. Decipher the message given below with the transposition key

    1 5 4 3 6 2 7 8.

    TEAEF OBHIT NERDC MOSHS SPCHT SIIYE EAATI RFERH YYDER
    EEMOE TPOIS FRNAR OESER TITDV OFMTT S

79. Decipher the message given below using the transposition key based on
    the word GEOMETRY.

    ILSOR ANSNE SUDUA CEFES HOTNO MAEAR HTOMM IHOIK GSTWE
    TTTCE HEYHH TIHTC DACTS WTNON KMEHS EG

5.4 Solution of incompletely filled rectangles— probable word method

The cryptanalyst who wishes to solve an incompletely filled columnar transposition has a much more difficult problem than in the
completely filled case. Even if he knows the length of the keyword
(which he still has to determine), he would not know which columns
are long and which are short. This complicates the problem of trying
to delimit strings of letters to form complete columns for anagramming.

It remains true though that if he can put together two letters
forming a correct digraph, then the strings of letters containing that
digraph will yield some correct combinations immediately above
and below it. If he can add to these digraphs a third string of letters
to form good trigraphs, he might be able to extend the text and
gradually derive a solution. For, as the text is extended, clues will be
derivable about the width of the rectangle and the proper lengths of
the columns both by the range within which good plain text combinations are found as well as by the study of the distances in the
cipher between letters that are adjacent in the plain text.

As our next example, we consider the problem of an incompletely
filled rectangle and the use of a probable word.

If the cryptanalyst had any information about the message which may lead to the correct assumption of a word in the text, it would provide him with a set of combinations to work towards and thus be of special help. Should the probable word be longer than the width of the rectangle, it would permit the determination of the number of columns.

To illustrate this point, suppose we have the following message to solve:

```
ARLHI KVENN UVHEV AMADF IWNDE YRTOS LTEND RTPET UVSIC
OESIL SDCTL NMAED NREHM HEYRD OEYEO ATNEE VAUHE GRTEE
SIEAS DNET
```

Suppose further that we have reason to believe that the word COMMUNISTS is contained in the text.

If the width of the rectangle is less than 10 columns, the word COMMUNISTS would occupy more than a full row and would therefore produce an overlap.

Assume the key to be nine digits long. Then, wherever in the rectangle the word COMMUNISTS would fall, the final S would be under the C. In transcription, the column containing the C would produce the cipher digraph CS. But there is no place in the cipher message where a C is followed by an S. If the word COMMUNISTS is in the message, the rectangle is not nine columns wide.

If the key length is eight, the word COMMUNISTS would cause an overlap of two letters and the cipher text would have to contain the digraphs CT and OS. Both these combinations occur, giving indication that the key may be eight letters long. It is possible, of course, that such pairs occur by chance. The cryptanalyst must keep in mind the possibility of accidental combinations and seek additional confirmation for his assumed text as he progresses. A check on each of the lengths less than eight shows that no such length admits the word COMMUNISTS.

Accepting the idea that the rectangle is eight columns wide and that the message contains the word COMMUNISTS, we can put together the two strings of letters containing the CT and OS combinations.

```
            EN
            SD
            IE
            LY
            SR
            DT
            CO
            TS
            LL
            NT
            ME
            AN
            ED
```

We have no idea yet how far we may go below and above our two known digraphs because we do not know where in the plain language message the word COMMUNISTS appears. We do know though from the length of the message (99 letters) that the columns are 12 or 13 letters long since 99 divided by 8 gives 12 plus a remainder of 3.

We also know that the O of CO must be followed by an M, and the T of TS must be preceded by an S. The M being much less frequent is a better choice for continuing. Although there are three M's in the message, only two need be considered since M of MAED is too close to the C in the cipher to be able to appear alongside the CO in the plain language.

Let us examine the two possibilities by writing the strings of letters containing the M's alongside the OS column and noting the resulting trigraphs (see facing page).

The right hand possibility is much better than the left. This can be confirmed statistically by listing the frequencies of the digraphs in the rightmost two columns of each set of trigraphs and by comparing the sums for the two cases. (The numbers listed result from rounding the actual frequencies shown in Appendix A to the nearest hundred.)

On examining the trigraphs formed we see the combination SDD, an impossible plain language combination. We would therefore assume

	Freq.			Freq.
ENU	1		ENE	5
SDV	0		SDD	0
IEH	0		IEN	10
LYE	1		LYR	0
SRV	1		SRE	13
DTA	4		DTH	22
COM			COM	
TSA	2		TSH	2
LLD	2		LLE	5
NTF	0		NTY	1
MEI	1		MER	14
ANW	0		AND	8
EDN	0		EDO	1
	12			81

that the columns do not extend above IEN. From the known information about the lengths of the columns, we can extend our strings of letters by two in the downward direction.

IEN
LYR
SRE
DTH
COM
TSH
LLE
NTY
MER
AND
EDO
DRE
NTY

Now the second of the two M's can be added.

```
IENH
LYRE
SREV
DTHA
COMM
TSHA
LLED
NTYF
MERI
ANDW
EDON
DRED
NTYE
```

These combinations are all good with the single exception of the IENH at the top of the column, which though not impossible is not very likely. We now seek a U to follow COMM. There are three, but it is quickly apparent that the best U is the first letter of the ninth group.

```
IENHT
LYREP
SREVE
DTHAT
COMMU
TSHAV
LLEDS
NTYFI
MERIC
ANDWO
EDONE
DREDS
NTYEI
```

We can now definitely discard the top line, so that the array we now have is the above array with the top line deleted.

The continuation of the anagramming procedure would call next for adding the N of the word COMMUNISTS, followed by the I and finally the S, to derive the complete plain language.

As an alternative approach, let us examine the following procedure. Suppose we mark off in the cipher message the columns already placed, and at the same time designate each of them with the number that belongs at the head of its column. These numbers progress consecutively because, in the enciphering process, the columns are transcribed in that order from the transposition rectangle.

1	2	3	4
ARLHIKVENNUVH	EVAMADFIWNDE	YRTOSLTENDRT	PETUVSICOESI

5	6	7	
LSDCTLNMAEDN	REHMHEYRDOEY	EOATNEEVAUHEGRTEESIEASDNET	

When we have done this we see that the strings of letters not yet included in our anagramming consist of a string of 13 letters representing column 1, and a string of 26 letters representing columns 7 and 8. We can divide the latter 26 letters into two sets of 13, and we can then place the three remaining columns alongside the already anagrammed columns.

	1	7	8
LYREP	A	E	R
SREVE	R	O	T
DTHAT	L	A	E
COMMU	H	T	E
TSHAV	I	N	S
LLEDS	K	E	I
NTYFI	V	E	E
MERIC	E	V	A
ANDWO	N	A	S
EDONE	N	U	D
DREDS	U	H	N
NTYEI	V	E	E
	H	G	T

The missing letters of the word COMMUNISTS appear on the fifth row of these last three columns and it is seen that they must be rearranged in the order 7 1 8.

Finally, since all the long columns of a transposition rectangle precede the short columns, the columns numbered 7, 1 and 8 belong on the left side of the rectangle.

```
7 1 8 5 3 6 2 4
E A R L Y R E P
O R T S R E V E
A L E D T H A T
T H E C O M M U
N I S T S H A V
E K I L L E D S
E V E N T Y F I
V E A M E R I C
A N S A N D W O
U N D E D O N E
H U N D R E D S
E V E N T Y E I
G H T
```

We now have the key and the plain text of the completed solution.

Exercises

Solve the following transpositions using the information given about a probable word contained in the message.

80. Probable word: LOS ANGELES

   HPYCR OEMDR SRIHD RNNSU YEAAE TSSED ETCCS FAIRN DAFTE
   OGSOM ETSCA ALLMO ERNIR PMEUF BA

81. Probable word: WASHINGTON

   NTHTL ASNAE TTOHE FMIPW TNTOO NKTGO EKINM HTSTO EIETT
   CHOYL HHCTM OMWEN GOEHM OCEET ILLAO DWFNE XNCEA EINTF
   IAL

5.5   Incompletely filled rectangles—general case

We have seen that if a word in the message is known, and in particular if it is longer than the width of the rectangle, solution by anagramming becomes possible.

   Consider now a columnar transposition problem for which we do not have a probable word.

GAELT CCRNT EOMEL EDOND GSBDH SOEDU HDAEE EEINT
TEEAQ UENES EGGTO EGPHI NNUUL SANEB YEAHM IESNA
RLBBV DE

This cipher has a quite special feature. It contains the letter Q.
This letter has the interesting property in English that it never ends
a word and is always followed by U, except in special abbreviations
like G.H.Q. or in proper names like Iraq. This fact provides a starting
point: we shall try to find a string of letters to combine with the set
including the Q. The U right next to the Q in the cipher could
not combine with it in the plain text. Therefore, the Q must be
followed by one of the three remaining U's. We are thus in the
fortunate situation of knowing that there are only three possibilities
we need to consider if we start with the digraph QU (assuming Q
is not a null).

If we set down a string of letters containing the Q —say we take
five on each side of it—we can then place alongside that string an
equally long string for each of the occurrences of the letter U.

T	H	P	H
T	S	H	I
E	O	I	N
E	E	N	N
A	D	N	U
Q	U	U	U
U	H	U	L
E	D	L	S
N	A	S	A
E	E	A	N
S	E	N	E

With good luck, the correct set of digraphs would be evident.
Without a clear indication of the right answer, we seek assistance by
examining the frequencies of the digraphs formed by juxtaposing
the strings of letters. To be sure, we are working somewhat in the
dark since we don't know how long the column should be nor how
the QU is positioned in it.

Accepting the idea of five above and five below, we set down the
frequencies of the various digraphs (see Appendix A) and we get

Digr.	Freq.	Digr.	Freq.	Digr.	Freq.
TH	22	TP	0	TH	22
TS	3	TH	22	TI	9
EO	0	EI	1	EN	10
EE	3	EN	10	EN	10
AD	3	AN	12	AU	1
QU		QU		QU	
UH	0	UU	0	UL	2
ED	9	EL	3	ES	9
NA	2	NS	3	NA	2
EE	3	EA	5	EN	10
SE	6	SN	0	SE	6
	51		56		81

The rightmost one seems best; it gives a much higher total than the other two columns and it is the only one of the three possibilities that has no very infrequent digraphs, i.e. there are no zero entries in that column. These are not infallible indications. It must be stressed again that we are dealing with statistical considerations. If we proceed with this possibility and make no progress, we may have to return and try the next best collection of digraphs.

The comment of page 77 about the use of log weights instead of monographic frequencies applies also to digraphs. It would require the replacement of each of the digraphic frequencies by its logarithm.

We have the following combinations:

TH
TI
EN
EN
AU
QU
UL
ES
NA
EN
SE

These digraphs give no assistance toward delimiting the columns because we can continue the columns in both directions and get possible combinations. We can get some help though in another way.

Suppose we have a message of n letters. In our example, $n = 87$. Then the dimensions r and c of the rectangle (where r denotes the number of rows, c the number of columns) must be such that

(5.1) $$n \leq r \cdot c.$$

The equality holds only when the rectangle is completely filled, and in that case all the columns are the same length. Otherwise, the short columns will have length $r - 1$, the long columns length r, and

(5.2) $$(r - 1) \cdot c < n < r \cdot c.$$

Now if we suspect that two letters, C_i and C_j, in our cipher message (in our example Q and U) are adjacent in the plain text, they will be in the same row (unless the first is at the end of a row and the second at the beginning of the next row, in which case our reasoning can be modified). Therefore, the difference $j - i$ in their positions in the cipher message ($j - i = 19$ in our example) is the sum of lengths of complete columns; i.e. it is obtainable as a sum consisting only of r's and $(r - 1)$'s.

For example, $19 = 10 + 9$, so one possibility is

(i) $$r = 10, \quad r - 1 = 9.$$

Also $19 = 7 + 6 + 6$, so another possibility is

(ii) $$r = 7, \quad r - 1 = 6.$$

From $19 = 5 + 5 + 5 + 4$, we find

(iii) $$r = 5, \quad r - 1 = 4,$$

etc.

Each of these possible values of r yields, by (5.2), an accompanying width c. Thus

(i) if $r = 10$, (5.2) implies $9c < 87 < 10c$, so $c = 9$;

(ii) if $r = 7$, (5.2) implies $6c < 87 < 7c$, so $c = 13$ or 14;

(iii) if $r = 5$, (5.2) implies $4c < 87 < 5c$, so $c = 18, 19, 20$ or 21,

etc.

These values of c furnish possible widths for the rectangle, that is, possible lengths of the keying sequence.

Suppose now that, in the inscription diagram, Q were in the rightmost column and U in the first column, but the next row down. Then the number of letters from U to the foot of its column would be one less than in the case where Q and U were on the same row, and in such an instance the sum of a number of complete long and short columns would be 18 instead of 19. This produces some additional possible rectangle widths which may have to be considered.

This kind of information about possible widths is not sufficient to assist us in extending the text we have put together thus far. What we must do now is seek a third string of letters to adjoin to our digraphs either to the right or to the left. Working to the right is preferable because we know that QU must be followed by a vowel. We also know that TH is very likely to be followed by an E, and TI is frequently followed by O (TIO is the third most frequent trigraph; TI is followed almost 50% of the time by O). We are prompted then to look for a place in the text where the combination EO...v occurs, the v standing for any vowel. There is one such place in the message. We adjoin the letters to our string of digraphs.

<pre>
THE
TIO
ENM
ENE
AUL
QUE
ULD
ESO
NAN
END
SEG
</pre>

All the trigraphs look possible, and we get very good combinations in several places. If we try to extend the columns beyond the range we have been working with we get NPT above the THE and EBS below the SEG. Neither of these looks like a possible plain text combination. It seems likely that the correct length of column is at most 11 ($r \leq 11$). It also seems probable from the large number of good trigraphs that the columns may be at least as long as 9 letters ($r \geq 9$). The interval in the cipher between the E of the QUE combination and the Q is 29 letters. We recall that one of our earlier calculations yielded $r = 10$. Combining these two facts leads to the conclusion that the columns are of lengths 9 and 10, and the width of the rectangle is 9. There must be two long columns and one short column between the E and the Q.

There are now two different ways in which we may continue.

a. We try with the already developed information to arrange tentative columns for anagramming. The E of THE which begins the string EOMEL . . . . . is position 11 of the cipher message and appears to be on the top row because the combination NPT above it has been discarded. Therefore, the first ten letters which constitute column 1 represent a long column. Two of the next three columns must be long and one short because the distance between E (in column 2) and Q (in column 5) is 29.

To represent this situation we write out the three columns 2, 3, 4 alongside the first, as follows:

```
    1 2 3 4

          D U
      G E G H
      A O S D
      E M B A
      L E D E
      T L H E
      C E S E
      C D O E
      R O E I
      N N D N
      T D U
```

The underlined letters may belong at the foot of one column or at the head of the next column, depending on which of columns 2, 3, 4 is the short one.

Next, we know from the interval 19 between Q (of column 5) and U (of column 7) that one of columns 5 and 6 is long and the other is short. We represent this as above, by writing down the columns with one letter taking either of two positions.

```
1 2 3 4 5 6 7

    D U   E
G E G H T   S
A O S D T   E
E M B A E   G
L E D E E   G
T L H E A   T
C E S E Q   O
C D O E U   E
R O E I E   G
N N D N N   P
T D U   E
```

Finally, only one of the last three columns is short because the total number of letters remaining is 29. We have now the array

```
1 2 3 4 5 6 7 8 9

    D U   E   N S
G E G H T S H E N
A O S D T E I B A
E M B A E G N Y R
L E D E E G N E L
T L H E A T U A B
C E S E Q O U H B
C D O E U E L M V
R O E I E G S I D
N N D N N P A E E
T D U   E   N S
```

with the underlined letters taking one of two possible positions.

Allowing for variations which may require moving some columns downward one position, we are now able to shift columns against one another for anagramming, as in the case of a completely filled rectangle.

b. Another possible procedure is to extend the text. For example, TIO is very frequently followed by N and we might hunt for a string of letters to add to our trigraphs which would give the tetragraph TION. After excluding those occurrences of N which enter into the columns already put together, the number of possibilities to be considered is small. Thus the N in position 9 cannot be used since it is close to the foot of the column. The N in position 19 has already been used. The N in position 39 is not possible because it too is at the foot of its column. On examination of all the occurrences of N, one finds that the only possible one to join on to the TIO is the letter in position 79. (Note in the previously derived array of columns for anagramming how clear it is that this is the only possible choice of the letter N.)

```
5 7 2 9

T H E S
T I O N
E N M A
E N E R
A U L L
Q U E B
U L D B
E S O V
N A N D
E N D E
S E G
```

The combinations formed with the addition of this column are excellent. We can begin to get suggestions for words, for example, the possible word QUEBEC. The proper E to adjoin to QUEB is quickly evident giving

```
5 7 2 9 4
T H E S U
T I O N H
E N M A D
E N E R A
A U L L E
Q U E B E
U L D B E
E S O V E
N A N D I
E N D E N
S E G
```

Then completing the word QUEBEC, we get to the solution of the message and the key

$$5\ 7\ 2\ 9\ 4\ 1\ 3\ 8\ 6$$

The solution which we have successfully achieved involved fortunate circumstances. The presence of a Q almost guaranteed that it would be followed by a U and made possible an initial set of digraphs with the help of which the text could be extended.

What is to be done if the rectangle is incompletely filled and there is no obvious entry by means of a pair of letters that must combine? An alternative could be to choose a pair of letters with a great affinity for one another like TH or RE and to try every such possible combination to fit two strings of letters together. If one of the letters of the digraph is infrequent—as for example in the combination VE —the number of possibilities is very considerably reduced. If the best fit is not readily evident, frequency calculations will assist in making a good choice.

A very general attack on a columnar transposition, not based on specific combinations of letters, might proceed as follows: Say we start with the beginning of the message. One end, namely the beginning, of column 1 is known and there is no problem of delimiting it in that direction. Take a group of letters starting with the beginning of the message and shift that string against every other similar length string to form digraphs. Some positions may be discarded at once because they include impossible combinations as, for example, V followed by a consonant. There will probably be few such impossible cases because it must be remembered that the first letter of a digraph may represent the end of one word and the second letter the beginning of another word.

In specially favorable situations, a specific set of digraphs may be such a good collection of frequent pairs that its correctness seems highly likely. In such a case, the next step would be to try to adjoin a third string of letters either before or after the good digraphs to form good trigraphs. The continuation of this procedure will gradually result in the reconstruction of the entire text.

Once two or three columns are correctly juxtaposed, whole words may be suggested, the lengths of the columns become clear, and the solution progresses at an increasing rate. The most difficult step is getting the first set of digraphs lined up.

To assist in this step we can record the frequency of every digraph and assign the total of these frequencies as a score to each possibility being considered. The highest score will hopefully correspond to the correct juxtaposition. Even if one result is not outstanding, this process will limit the likely possibilities to a small number.

We shall not present an illustration of this procedure here, because it is lengthy and consists largely of trial and error. It is however theoretically feasible and will achieve a solution, given a sufficient amount of time.

Exercise

82. Solve the following transposition which is suspected to contain the word EARTHQUAKE.

```
DPSEW NKKWR EEILG UOSIA ANLEA HAKAD SMLAQ TAESA NOIAO
TEIIA OMHHL ITREW TGEPE FWDFF ATCES TDDLD RICTH EAIHE
WLE
```

5.6 Repetitions between messages; identical length messages

It would appear then that a columnar transposition with an incompletely filled rectangle may sometimes have the capability of delaying solution, perhaps even for a reasonably long period of time. This is likely to be true if there is only one message for study. If there are many messages in the same key then special situations sometimes arise which serve as a great aid in solution.

We shall consider two such situations. Consider first the possibility that each of two messages contains the same long plain text phrase. Then this fact can be recognized and utilized to achieve a solution.

To illustrate, suppose the following cipher messages have been intercepted:

1. FRIIT ECESE ONEAS DHLIS NTTDR CONML RDONR SDDSM
   AFGHI HHTTA ONDAT ELTAB TETMA YVRTS NYADE EIOTI
   AACAE EHLMS ARETE INRE

2. ANART AONIN SDBEH LMONT BATRE ASIOE EOPET MNEPT
   ITTDD SCNEI SEYRC OTEOT UOFRI NCLAL HBEEI OT

A trigraphic frequency study of these messages reveals eight repetitions, shown by underlines in the texts.

The cause of these repetitions seems clear. What has happened is that columnar transpositions of the same width (and we shall assume they have the same key) have been applied to two messages both containing the same long phrase. The phrase appears in different parts of the two rectangles. As a result, the letters of that phrase which appear in a particular column of one message will be found in a different column of the other message. That is why the repeated groups of letters enter into different positions in the two messages.

There are eight repeated sequences (5 trigraphs, 2 tetragraphs, 1 pentagraph); these indicate that there are 8 columns in the transposition rectangles of both messages, and that the repeated phrase probably occupies at least three lines, so it contains at least 24 letters.

Knowing the width of the rectangles, we can calculate the number of long and short columns in each message. The first message has 99 letters. Dividing 99 by 8 gives a quotient of 12 and a remainder of 3. This means that the first message has 3 columns of 13 letters each and 5 columns of length 12. The second message has 77 letters. It must therefore have 5 columns of length 10 and 3 columns of length 9.

Further, since the letters FRI at the beginning of the first message are part of the repeated phrase, the long repetition must begin on the first line of the 8×13 rectangle containing the plain text of message 1. It may even be the very beginning of the message. In the second message, the long repetition must appear within the interior of the message because the letters TAO of column 1 have other letters on both sides of them within the column.

Let us now record the columnar portions of the long repetition in both messages with an indication of the key number which pertains to each column. We know the key numbers because the transcription of the cipher message from the original rectangle is in consecutive order. We have then:

Message 1		Message 2	
1	FRI	1	TAON
2	EAS	2	EHLM
3	RCO	3	EAS
4	DDS	4	ETM
5	TAON	5	DDS
6	ETM	6	RCO
7	EEIOT	7	FRI
8	EHLM	8	EEIOT

Suppose that the first letter of the two occurrences of the repeated phrase are x columns apart in the two inscription diagrams. Then that same statement will be true for any common letter of the repeated phrase; its positions in the two messages will be separated by x letters.

So since FRI in Message 1 occurs in column 1, it must follow that column 7, which is where we find FRI in Message 2, must be x columns away from column 1 in the inscription rectangle. And since EAS is in column 2 of Message 1 and column 3 of Message 2, column 3 must be x places removed from column 2. A similar statement can be made for any two columns containing the same portion of the repeated phrase.

We can therefore go through a chaining process of following each column number of Message 1 by the number of the column in Message 2 which contains the same letters of the repetition. The resulting cycle (1, 7, 8, 2, 3, 6, 4, 5) is such that each consecutive pair of numbers represents columns the same distance apart in the original rectangle. But that must mean that this sequence of numbers is a decimation of the transposition key.

All we need to do now to solve the messages is to determine the interval of decimation. For, once this is known we can reconstruct the original transposition key. One way to do this would be to try every decimation in turn. The correct one will produce plain language.

Alternatively we can inscribe the text into a rectangle with the sequence we have developed as key. If we do this for the first message, making the first letter of each repetition portion the head of its column, we get

```
1 7 8 2 3 6 4 5

F E E E R E D T
R E H A C T D A
I I L S O M S O
I O M D N A M N
T T S H M Y A D
E I A L L V F A
C A R I R R G T
E A E S D T H E
S C T N O S I L
E A E T N N H T
O E I T R Y H A
N   N D S A T B
    R     D   T
    E
```

There is a problem about columns 7 and 8. The first is too short, the second too long. This must mean that the letter E at the head of key column 8 belongs at the foot of key column 7. It just happens that that letter E is an accidental repetition and not part of the repeated phrase. We make the adjustment.

```
1 7 8 2 3 6 4 5

F E H E R E D T
R E L A C T D A
I I M S O M S O
I O S D N A M N
T T A H M Y A D
E I R L L V F A
C A E I R R G T
E A T S D T H E
S C E N O S I L
E A I T N N H T
O E N T R Y H A
N E R D S A T B
    E     D   T
```

The three long columns must belong at the left end of the diagram. They are headed by the letters HET which suggest that the first word is THE. Therefore the correct key begins 5 8 6 and is the decimation of the previously derived sequence at interval 3. It is

$$5 \ 8 \ 6 \ 1 \ 2 \ 4 \ 7 \ 3$$

Application of this key will decipher the message.

The second special situation which we shall describe is applicable to any type of transposition system. It depends on the availability of two or more messages of identical length and all in the same key. In such a set of messages, no matter how complicated the transposition system may have been, letters having the same position numbers in the plain text messages will have the same position numbers in the cipher messages. If the messages are super-imposed so that the first letters of all the messages are in one column, the second letters in a second column, etc. the solution procedure will consist of anagramming entire columns. For example, if five messages are available, columns of five letters each can be used in the anagramming process.

If, for example, it is assumed that two particular letters of one of the messages are adjacent in the plain text, then the columns containing them should give good combinations. When a good set of digraphs has been found, a third letter may be added to produce good trigraphs, etc. Once a good start has been made, extensions to the columns already put together will become easier as the solution progresses. And, as in the case of columnar transposition, the method of summing frequencies can be a helpful tool.

If the number of messages of identical length available for study is large, a solution by anagramming is reasonably certain to be achieved. But this does not imply that we can necessarily solve messages of other lengths. To accomplish this with the key resulting from the identical length messages, it would be necessary to develop information about the general system and the method by which the specific keys are assigned, before being able to cope with messages of other lengths.

Exercises

83. Solve the following messages which were sent from the same point of origin:

    1. ATDCC ITSFA IAEIT EARTF RTARL NRNAL RCUOY SSEHO STNNC
       OTTER AOTSU UITDS FEHTI RWPOT RNEEN TNAER TIISO LOIRI
       BONUI OEAEE

    2. EENNI ERILA HTICY SRSJT NUIDO TETSE ITOAV DROHU OYNUO
       AARUI SOEAE IDAST ARLBU ELOTT SUMNY SSNDN NCDNT YIDRD
       CCEMS ANAY

84. The following message includes the words PRESIDENT JOHNSON.

    EHENA FONEG SROTE IXTIE ISAAT SASPJ IHNII NCDON REEAE
    EHSYN TMADT STRSN ZLSNM EEYME TENOF EV

85. Probable words: UNITED STATES.

    AVEUT DTSTH SONGP NSITE ABEIF TESTN TESCL SHADM DOFSR
    DRTEI EDOMT EOIYN MNRNE SLOSE CTEAF OEUET AMELH KNPLT
    TROOD DRUDP UEYIF L

86. Solve:

    LNTIO PANSC RNIEE STUEE NCEYR AENCA SVCDL OEPSE NCOHT
    IOPLH RDMNL VMISC RGYHE FTYAO EUEYD OTHEF TPDCE YASPE
    IAS

87. Solve:

    ACNNT LHENT PSOAC TEETE EETRC OMUNC TVNRE EGBNS INRSV
    ERERU OIRII SOHOT SRMOD TESBB DAEFO CSDEL MREDT OMUEO
    NIERY Y

APPENDIX A

Table of digraphic frequencies

1st \ 2nd	·A	·B	·C	·D	·E	·F	·G	·H	·I	·J	·K	·L	·M	·N	·O	·P	·Q	·R	·S	·T	·U	·V	·W	·X	·Y	·Z
A·	7	125	251	304	13	65	151	13	311	13	67	681	182	1216	5	144	0	764	648	1019	89	137	37	17	202	15
B·	114	7	2	1	394	0	0	0	74	7	0	152	6	0	118	0	0	81	28	6	87	2	0	0	143	0
C·	319	2	52	1	453	0	0	339	202	0	86	98	4	3	606	0	1	113	23	237	92	0	15	3	25	0
D·	158	1	1	33	572	1	20	1	273	5	0	0	27	8	111	0	25	49	75	2	91	15	6	0	40	0
E·	492	27	323	890	326	106	93	16	118	4	27	340	253	1029	326	143	0	1436	917	301	36	160	153	113	90	3
F·	98	0	0	0	150	108	0	0	188	0	1	35	2	1	129	0	0	142	3	4	54	0	0	0	5	0
G·	122	0	0	2	271	0	20	145	95	0	0	23	3	51	287	0	0	150	29	58	58	0	4	0	6	0
H·	646	2	5	3	2053	0	0	0	426	0	0	0	184	14	45	0	0	56	10	28	31	0	0	0	15	0
I·	236	51	476	285	271	80	174	7	10	0	31	352	1	1550	7	62	5	212	741	704	54	155	0	15	20	49
J·	18	1	0	0	26	0	0	0	0	0	0	0	0	0	0	0	0	0	0	0	48	0	0	0	0	0
K·	14	1	0	1	187	1	0	6	56	0	0	7	0	20	0	0	0	0	39	1	1	0	0	0	0	0
L·	359	5	6	197	513	28	29	0	407	0	4	378	22	1	208	11	0	9	104	68	72	15	0	0	219	0
M·	351	65	5	761	573	2	0	14	259	0	0	22	126	8	240	139	3	5	47	1	65	1	8	0	37	0
N·	249	2	281	130	549	46	630	42	301	0	21	33	47	88	239	2	0	5	340	743	56	31	194	5	71	2
O·	48	57	91	21	21	731	46	0	52	0	30	208	397	1232	125	164	0	861	201	756	533	188	0	1	23	2
P·	241	0	1	0	310	0	0	8	75	0	0	144	139	1	268	103	3	409	32	51	81	0	8	7	0	0
Q·	0	0	0	0	0	0	0	0	0	0	0	0	0	0	0	0	0	0	0	0	73	0	0	0	0	0
R·	470	15	79	129	1280	14	80	0	541	0	44	75	139	149	510	25	0	97	300	273	88	65	13	0	140	0
S·	200	4	94	9	595	8	0	186	390	0	94	48	37	7	234	128	0	295	277	823	192	2	45	0	27	0
T·	381	2	22	1	872	4	1	2161	865	0	30	62	9	9	756	2	0	306	257	131	120	3	0	0	125	0
U·	72	87	103	51	91	11	80	2	54	0	1	230	69	318	4	81	0	13	256	263	6	1	0	2	3	3
V·	65	0	0	2	522	0	0	0	223	0	0	5	1	44	46	0	0	0	2	0	1	0	3	0	5	1
W·	282	1	15	4	239	0	0	175	259	0	1	5	44	0	159	47	0	9	45	2	0	0	0	0	3	0
X·	9	0	3	2	17	0	0	1	15	0	0	0	1	5	1	9	0	2	0	23	2	5	0	0	0	0
Y·	17	1	0	0	84	0	0	0	20	0	0	1	11	0	64	0	0	0	44	5	1	5	3	5	2	1
Z·	18	0	0	0	36	0	0	0	17	0	0	0	0	0	4	0	0	0	0	0	0	0	0	0	0	2

APPENDIX B

Log Weights

A	1.863	N	1.892
B	0.954	O	1.869
C	1.477	P	1.431
D	1.644	Q	0.477
E	2.114	R	1.887
F	1.447	S	1.799
G	1.204	T	1.969
H	1.544	U	1.431
I	1.869	V	1.114
J	0.301	W	1.204
K	0.477	X	0.699
L	1.544	Y	1.279
M	1.398	Z	0.000

APPENDIX C

Frequencies of the letters of the alphabet in a sample of 1000 letters, arranged alphabetically and by frequency.

A	73		E	130
B	9		T	93
C	30		N	78
D	44		R	77
E	130		I	74
F	28		O	74
G	16		A	73
H	35		S	63
I	74		D	44
J	2		H	35
K	3		L	35
L	35		C	30
M	25		F	28
N	78		P	27
O	74		U	27
P	27		M	25
Q	3		Y	19
R	77		G	16
S	63		W	16
T	93		V	13
U	27		B	9
V	13		X	5
W	16		K	3
X	5		Q	3
Y	19		J	2
Z	1		Z	1

178

APPENDIX D

Frequencies of letters as initial letters of 16,410 words of newspaper text, arranged alphabetically and by frequency.

A	1802		T	2614
B	757		A	1802
C	918		S	1213
D	459		O	1176
E	410		I	922
F	666		C	918
G	293		W	833
H	636		P	768
I	922		B	757
J	95		F	666
K	88		H	636
L	348		M	578
M	578		R	513
N	401		D	459
O	1176		E	410
P	768		N	401
Q	31		L	348
R	513		G	293
S	1213		U	224
T	2614		Y	126
U	224		V	100
V	100		J	95
W	833		K	88
X	10		Q	31
Y	126		X	10
Z	6		Z	6

APPENDIX E

Frequencies of letters as final letters of 16,410 words of newspaper text, arranged alphabetically and by frequency.

A	480		E	3325
B	25		S	2077
C	107		D	1649
D	1649		N	1592
E	3325		T	1587
F	744		R	906
G	463		Y	903
H	407		O	745
I	72		F	744
J	6		L	599
K	148		A	480
L	599		G	463
M	220		H	407
N	1592		M	220
O	745		W	166
P	84		K	148
Q	1		C	107
R	906		P	84
S	2077		I	72
T	1587		X	34
U	29		U	29
V	15		B	25
W	166		V	15
X	34		J	6
Y	903		Z	5
Z	5		Q	1

Solutions to Exercises

1. COWARDS DIE MANY TIMES BEFORE THEIR DEATHS

2. THE EVIL THAT MEN DO LIVES AFTER THEM

3. (a) Wednesday (b) 1/4

4. $x = 1$ **5.** $y = 2$

6. (a) AOL MHBSA KLHY IYBABZ PZ UVA PU VBY ZAHYZ IBA PU VBYZLSCLZ

(b) THERE IS A TIDE IN THE AFFAIRS OF MEN WHICH TAKEN AT THE FLOOD LEADS ON TO FORTUNE

7. $K = 9$ **8.** $K = 21$ **9.** $K = 14$ **10.** $K = 5$

11. (a) $y = 10$ (b) $x = 2, 5, 8$

12. 3

13. Any multiple of 2 or 3
Any number having a factor in common with n

14. (a) Interval 7

(b)

Plain	A B C D E F G H I J K L M N O P Q R S T U V W X Y Z
Cipher	G N U B I P W D K R Y F M T A H O V C J Q X E L S Z

(c) ORDER IS HEAVENS FIRST LAW

15. $C = 9P$ **16.** $C = 5P$ **17.** (a) 8 (b) 5 (c) 4

18. (a) $x = 2, 5$ and 8 (b) $x = 1$ and 14

19. (a) 5 (b) 3 (c) 21 **20.** $C = 7P$ **21.** $C = 9P + 4$

22. $C = P + 7$ **23.** $C = 21P + 11$ **24.** $C = 25P + 1$

25. $C = 11P + 2$ **26.** $C = P + 15$ **27.** $C = 7P + 7$

28. (a) SECRET MESSAGE   (b) UNITED NATIONS

(c) UNITED STATES   (d) WIRELESS

(e) NEW YORK TIMES

In Exercises 29–32, cipher sequences are transposed keyword mixed, based on:

29. SIGNAL   **30.** UNIVERSITY

31. GONE WITH THE WIND   **32.** SUNDOWN

33. SHORT WAVE BROADCASTING CARRIES FURTHER THAN THAT USING REGULAR WAVES IT IS USED BY AMATEURS AND IN FREQUENCY MODULATION AND FOR TRANS-OCEANIC TELEPHONY

34. OF ALL THE STARS THE SUN IS NEAREST TO THE EARTH AND IT IS THE CENTER OF THE SOLAR SYSTEM ALL THE PLANETS MOVE AROUND IT

35. FEMALES OF SOME BREEDS OF SHEEP WEIGH AS LITTLE AS ONE HUNDRED POUNDS OTHER EWES MAY WEIGH OVER TWO HUNDRED TWENTY POUNDS

In Exercises 36–40, the plain sequence is normal, the keyword for the cipher sequence (all cipher sequences are transposed keyword mixed) is:

36. HUMAN   **37.** MILLIONAIRE   **38.** PHONETICS

39. BLUESTOCKING   **40.** WASHINGTON

41. THE CHAIRMAN OF THE FEDERAL RESERVE BOARD SAID YESTERDAY THAT A TAX INCREASE IS NEEDED NOW

42. The I.C.'s are: p. 28: .085   p. 34: .061

43. These distributions come from cipher messages involving, respectively, the following numbers of alphabets:

	(1)	(2)	(3)	(4)	(5)
No. of alphabets:	7	1	5	1	26
I.C.:	.041	.064	.042	.076	.037

44. 7   **45.** 5

46. Plain sequence: normal   **47.** Plain sequence: normal
   Cipher sequence: normal   Cipher sequence: normal
   Keyword: SOLVING   Keyword: WHIST

48. A of distribution 1 against S of distribution 2. I. C. is .076.

49. A of distribution 1 against Y of distribution 2. I.C. is .078.

50. Yes. The two combined distributions will match with W of 49 against A of 48.

51. There would be *no* coincidences between the two messages.

52. Keyword for plain sequence: JOHNS
   Keyword for cipher sequence: HOPKINS

In Exercises 53–61, unless otherwise noted, all mixed sequences are transposed keyword mixed

	Plain Sequence	Cipher Sequence	Keyword for Selection of Alphabets	Alignment (key letters set against)
53.	Normal	Normal	BROKEN	A_p
54.	Normal	Normal	THUNDER	A_p
55.	PHILOSOPHY (not trans.)	Normal	VINEGAR	A_p
56.	AGRICULTURE	Normal	FARMS	A_p
57.	Normal	EARTHQUAKES (not trans.)	ISTANBUL	A_p
58.	UNIVERSITY	Normal	PICTURE	U_p
59.	MONSTER	Normal	MARYLAND	M_p
60.	UNDERWATER	HYDROGRAPHY	HONEY	U_p
61.	PEANUTS	CARTOON	(1) FUDGE	P_p
			(2) AMERICA	P_p

62. DIFFICULTIES ARE THINGS THAT SHOW WHAT MEN ARE

63. IRRATIONALLY HELD TRUTHS MAY BE MORE HARMFUL THAN REASONED ERRORS

64. (a) $\begin{pmatrix} 23 & 12 \\ 26 & 23 \end{pmatrix}$ (b) $\begin{pmatrix} 11 & 24 \\ 20 & 9 \end{pmatrix}$

65. (a) 5 (b) 1 (c) 18 (d) 9

66. (a) $\begin{pmatrix} 3 & 24 \\ 19 & 5 \end{pmatrix}$ (b) $\begin{pmatrix} 24 & 5 \\ 19 & 14 \end{pmatrix}$ (c) $\begin{pmatrix} 4 & 11 \\ 1 & 22 \end{pmatrix}$

67. (a) 3 (b) (i) it has no inverse (ii) 7 (iii) 3

68. (a) 3 (b) 4   **69.** (a) 24 (b) 11 (c) 8   **70.** CIDECI

71. $\begin{pmatrix} 3 & 4 \\ 11 & 23 \end{pmatrix}$ **72.** $\begin{pmatrix} 7 & 3 \\ 10 & 19 \end{pmatrix}$ **73.** $\begin{pmatrix} 3 & 9 \\ 2 & 23 \end{pmatrix}$

74. THE THREE GENERAL REGIONS OF THE SOUTH PACIFIC ARE POLYNESIA MICRONESIA AND MELANESIA

75. THE HIGH ISLANDS OF THE SOUTH PACIFIC ARE THE EXPOSED SUMMITS OF SUBMERGED VOLCANOES

76. Keyword: JOHNSON   **77.** Keyword: CHESSBOARD

78. THE SENATE YESTERDAY APPROVED A CODE OF ETHICS FOR ITS MEMBERS FOR THE FIRST TIME IN HISTORY

79. HIGH SCHOOL STUDENTS TODAY KNOW MUCH MORE MATHEMATICS THAN THE WISEST OF THE ANCIENT GREEKS

80. Keyword: RAINBOW   **81.** Keyword: MENDING

82. Key: 7 10 3 9 8 6 4 2 5 1

83. Keyword for both messages: LEGITIMATE

84. Keyword: INVARIANT   **85.** Keyword: REPUBLICAN

86. Keyword: WORLD   **87.** Keyword: GEOMETRY

Suggestions for Further Reading

Cryptology

Apart from the first book listed below there is nothing available in English on methods of cryptanalysis. Most of the books that have been published on cryptology tell about the history and the drama of events in which cryptanalysis played a significant role. Those listed have been specifically chosen because they do include some indication of how solutions were achieved.

Gaines, H. F., *Cryptanalysis*, Dover, New York, 1956.

A non-mathematical treatment of methods for solving cryptograms. Systems studied are much the same as those covered in this text.

Kahn, David, *The Code Breakers*, Macmillan, New York, 1967.

A comprehensive history of cryptology from earliest times to the 1900's. Includes also a great deal about cryptologic events prior to and during World War II.

Pratt, Fletcher, *Secret and Urgent*, Blue Ribbon Books, Garden City, N.Y., 1942.

This book describes a variety of historical situations in which secret language played a significant part. It includes a number of tables giving information about frequencies in English and in four European languages. There is also a list of common pattern words in English.

Yardley, H. O., *The American Black Chamber*, Bobbs Merrill, Indianapolis, 1931.

This book tells about some of the successes of an official U. S. cryptanalytic service during the years 1919–1928. The various situations described concern diplomatic communications.

Cleator, P. E., *Lost Languages*, Mentor Books, New American Library, New York, 1959.

The story of how cryptanalytic principles assisted in the reconstruction of such dead languages as Egyptian hieroglyphics, cuneiform, Minoan Linear B.

Friedman, William F. and Elizabeth S., *The Shakespearean Ciphers Examined*, Cambridge University Press, England, 1957.

A scholarly cryptanalytic study and refutation of the possibility of hidden ciphers in the Shakespearean plays.

Modular Arithmetic

LeVeque, W. J., *Topics in Number Theory*, Vol. 1, Addison Wesley, Reading, Mass., 1956.

Gardner, K. L., *Discovering Modern Algebra*, Oxford University Press, 1966. (Also includes material on permutations and matrices)

Griffin, Harriet, *Elementary Theory of Numbers*, McGraw Hill, New York, 1954.

Probability and Statistics

Mosteller, F., Rourke, R. E. K., Thomas, G. B., *Probability with Statistical Applications*, Addison Wesley, Reading, Mass., 1961.

Mendenhall, W., *Introduction to Probability and Statistics*, Wadsworth Publishing Co., Belmont, Calif., 1967.

Hoyt, J. P., *Probability Theory*, International Textbook Co., Scranton, Penna., 1967.

Matrices

School Mathematics Study Group, *Introduction to Matrix Algebra*, Yale University Press, New Haven, 1961.

Davis, P. J., *The Mathematics of Matrices*, Blaisdell, Waltham, Mass., 1965.

Bowman, F., *Introduction to Determinants and Matrices*, English Universities Press, 1962.

Permutations

Burnside, W., *Theory of Groups of Finite Order*, Dover, New York, 1955.

Carmichael, R. D., *Introduction to the Theory of Groups of Finite Order*, Dover, New York, 1956.

INDEX